AUTISM
COMMUNICATION KEYS

Always Advocating, Celebrating
Neurodiversity, And Fostering Inclusivity

Kim Gallo SLP
Speech-Language Pathologist

A CHAT WITH THE SPEECH THERAPIST

Give Them The Words

The Pivot for Parents and Educators: ADHD/Autism

A CHAT WITH THE

SPEECH THERAPIST

ADVICE FOR PARENTS OF SMART,
LATE-TALKINGCHILDREN

KIM GALLO M.S., CCC-SLP
SPEECH LANGUAGE PATHOLOGIST

Disclaimer Notice:

ABOUT THE AUTHOR

While earning a bachelor's degree in Psychology in the late 90s, Kim Gallo worked alongside Certified Behavior Analysts teaching young toddlers newly diagnosed with autism. She then earned Board Certification as an Associate Behavior Analyst. In 2004, Kim earned a Master's degree in Speech-Language Pathology. In 2005, she completed her fellowship and earned her
Certificate of Clinical Competence (CCC), thus becoming certified by the American Speech and Hearing Association. She has worked in various settings on multidisciplinary teams with the Early Intervention program, in K-12 schools, and in private
practice with children and young adults. Kim is also the parent of two children, one of whom is a neurodivergent young adult.

For even more resources:
kimgalloslp.com

INTRODUCTION

If you are a parent who is concerned that your child is not meeting their developmental milestones, you may be experiencing feelings of concern or anxiety. You may be worrying that your child is not developing at the same rate as other children their age or that they may have a developmental delay or disorder. You may also be concerned about how this could impact your child's future, such as in school or social situations. Additionally, some parents may feel a sense of guilt or wonder if they are doing something wrong. Parents need to understand that every child develops at their own pace and that there is a wide range of what is considered "normal." However, seeking early intervention from a doctor or developmental specialist, such as a speech-language pathologist, can help address any concerns and support a child's growth and development. There are many things that parents can do to help foster language development. We will explore some of them here.

CHAPTER 1

EARLY INTERVENTION PROGRAMS (BIRTH–THREE YEARS)

After a conversation with a spouse, a friend, or a family member, a parent's next step is likely to bring their concerns about speech development to the child's pediatrician. The pediatrician may give a referral to a local early intervention program, and they may suggest or perform a hearing screening. Alternatively, in the US, a parent can call their state's EI program to learn more about having a child evaluated. Again, they will probably require a hearing screening before an evaluation occurs. The early intervention program aims to have family-centered, community-based, coordinated services with measurable, functional outcomes that will improve family life and possibly reduce the need for specialized education when a child reaches school age.

Early intervention speech therapy is designed to be fun and engaging for the child. It usually involves the therapist teaching parents play activities to encourage language development. The therapist works with the child and the family or daycare to set goals and create a personalized therapy plan.

The therapy will likely target some of the following objectives:

- cognitive skills (thinking, learning, problemsolving)
- communication skills (gesturing, talking, listening, understanding)
- physical and sensory skills (crawling, walking, climbing, seeing, hearing)
- social-emotional skills (playing, understanding feelings, making friends)
- adaptive or self-help skills (eating, bathing, dressing)

With the help of an early intervention speech therapist, children can gain the communication skills they need to succeed in a school and community setting. For example, suppose a child is between three and five years of age. In that case, the parent can contact their local school district and ask about the "Child-Find" program, also known as 'Part B.' Like the Early Intervention program, the Child-Find program has professionals who can evaluate and recommend therapy or schooling if the child qualifies. Then, when a child is ready for kindergarten, typically after their fifth birthday, if services are still required, the childstudy team at the elementary school will meet with the parent, and an individualized educational plan may be written and implemented.

CHAPTER 2

BEFORE THEY SPEAK

Before children start speaking, their brains go through various stages to develop language. These stages are critical to their ability to produce meaningful language and communicate effectively withothers. Here are some of the essential requirements that kids need to do before they can talk:

Listening and understanding: Children need to develop the ability to understand language before producing it themselves. Therefore, they need to be exposed to a rich language environment where they can hear different types of language and learn the patterns and rules of the language they are acquiring. One way to accomplish this is to narrate what you are doing throughout the day. For example, "Mommy is washing the dishes," or "I'm using my key to open up the door," "Let's put your pants on," then count "one and two" as you pull each foot through the pant leg.

Imitate sounds: Children also need to start imitating the sounds they hear around them, even if they don't fully understand their meaning. Imitating sounds helps them develop their speech muscles and begin associating sounds with objects and events. Kids usually start talking by making the sound "da"—it's not precisely dad, but it's the perfect start. So think about that when you are encouraging language.

Play with sounds: Children who imitate sounds must also play with sounds. This type of play involves repeating and experimenting with different sounds, syllables, and words, which helps them refine their speech and become more confident in their communication skills. For example, instead of attempting to get your child to say the word car, as part of the pretend play of moving the car, say "mmmmmm" in hopes they will imitate the more effortless sound.

Children must also recognize social cues: Such as eyecontact and body language, when communicating with others. Attention to social cues helps them to understand the social context of communication and adjust behavior accordingly. For example, Peek-A-Boo and I'm Gonna Getcha (a chasing game) are great simple games to develop these skills.

Develop an understanding of nonverbal communication: In addition to paying attention to social cues, children must understand nonverbal communication, such as gestures, facial expressions, and body language. This understanding will help them better understand the meaning of what others are communicating, even when they are not speaking.

Build vocabulary: As children continue developing their language skills, they must learn new words and phrases. Vocabulary growth is critical to their communication ability, enabling them to express their thoughts and ideas more precisely and clearly.

Develop grammatical skills: Children also need to learn to put words together in meaningful ways because it helps them create more complex sentences and convey more nuanced meanings.

Practice speaking: Children must practice speaking and communicating with others. This practice helps them refine their language skills and become more confident in communicating effectively. So, as you can see, a lot must happen before children begin communicating verbally. First, they must gothrough various stages of language development, including listening and understanding, imitating sounds, and playing with sounds.They must pay attention to social cues, understand nonverbal communication, and build their vocabulary. Eventually, they will be able to develop grammatical skills and practice speaking. By supporting children through these stages and providing them with a rich language environment, parents and caregivers can help them become confident communicators.

CHAPTER 3

WHAT IS JOINT ATTENTION ?

Joint attention is a critical component of social interaction and plays a crucial role in developing social skills in toddlers. It refers to the shared focus of two individuals on an object or event, which helps to establish communication and common ground between them.

Joint attention is a complex social phenomenon that developegradually in most toddlers and is related to the development of several cognitive, social, and emotional abilities. Around the age of nine months, infants start to show their first signs of joint attention, such as following the gaze of others and pointing to objects of interest. By eighteen months, most toddlers can engage in simple joint attention, such as sharing attention with others on an object or event. As they continue to grow and develop, they become increasingly skilled at joint attention and can use it more effectively to communicate with others and coordinate their activities.

One of the main benefits of joint attention is that it helps to facilitate communication and social interaction between toddlers and their caregivers. When two individuals are engaged in joint attention, they can share experiences and understand each other's perspectives, which is critical for building relationships and social connections. Joint attention also helps toddlers develop their language skills, as they can learn from others and use gestures, pointing, and eye gaze to communicate with them.

In addition to its benefits, there are also challenges associated with joint attention in toddlers. Some toddlers may struggle with joint attention due to underlying developmental difficulties, such as attention deficit/ hyperactivity disorder (ADHD), autism, or other conditions. These toddlers may face extra challenges in knowing how to engage in joint attention, following the gaze of others, or understanding the perspectives of others. These challenges can lead to difficulties in social interaction and communication. That's not to say that establishing joint attention in those populations isn't possible. Caregivers must learn how to "share the moments" differently, and speech-language pathologists are trained to teach parents how to establish joint attention in these populations.

To support the development of joint attention in toddlers, caregivers must engage in activities encouraging shared engagement and social interaction. For example, playing games that involve pointing and looking, reading books together, and participating in shared activities such as cooking or playing with toys can help develop joint attention. Additionally, it may be helpful for caregivers to provide structured routines and opportunities for social interaction, such as regularly scheduled playdates or visits with friends and family.

Joint attention is a critical component of social interaction and plays a crucial role in developing social skills in toddlers. It develops gradually over time and is related to the development of several cognitive, social, and emotional abilities. While there are benefits associated with joint attention, there are also challenges that some toddlers may face, such as difficulties with attention or social interaction. To support the development of joint attention, caregivers need to engage in activities that encourage shared attention and social interaction.

Here are twelve ways to practice joint attention skills in toddlers:

- **Following the child's gaze:** When your child is looking at something, look at it too.
- **Pointing:** Point at objects and ask your child to look at them Pointing helps the child learn to follow your gaze and attend to what you are looking at.
- **Reading books:** Read books with your child and point at the pictures. This helps your child learn to focus on the images while you read. Pause once in a while to get the child to reference you (look at your face).
- **Playing games:** Play games that involve looking and pointing, such as "I Spy."
- **Using gestures:** Use gestures such as nodding or waving to get your child's attention. Sometimes it's best to change it up, stop talking, and try to communicate via gestures such as nodding your head or gesturing, "come here."

- **Using routines:** such as mealtime or bath time to practice joint attention.
- **Singing songs:** Sing songs and act out the actions in the song.
- **Using toys:** Use toys that involve joint attention, such as balls that you and your child can throw back and forth.
- **Imitating:** Imitate your child's actions and wait for them to imitate you.
- **Using eye contact:** Make eye contact with your child and hold it for a few seconds.
- **Using mirrors:** Play with mirrors to help your child learn to attend to their actions.
- **Using technology:** Use videos and apps that involve joint attention and following instructions.

CHAPTER 4

SPEECH OR LANGUAGE

Speech and language are two distinct but related concepts in communication. While they are often used interchangeably, there are essential differences between speech and language that are important to understand.

Language refers to symbols, rules, and conventions used by a particular community to communicate meaning. It includes both spoken and written forms of communication and nonverbal forms such as gestures, facial expressions, and body language. Language is a complex system that allows us to express abstractthoughts, emotions, and ideas, and it is present in all human cultures.

On the other hand, speech refers to the actual verbal sounds produced by the human vocal apparatus. It is a form of language expression that involves articulating speech sounds, or phonemes, to create words and sentences. Speech is a physical activity that requires coordination of the mouth, tongue, and vocal cords, and it is an essential component of language, but it isnot the only one.

Another difference between speech and language is their

developmental patterns. While children typically begin speaking before fully understanding language, language development occurs gradually over the first several years of life. Children first learn to recognize familiar sounds and words and then use simple words and phrases to express their needs and wants.

Over time, they develop more complex language skills, such as forming grammatically correct sentences, understanding abstract concepts, and using figurative language.

Speech and language also differ in their clinical implications. Speech disorders refer to difficulties in producing speech sounds, while language disorders refer to challenges in understanding or using language. For example, a person with a speech disorder may have trouble pronouncing words correctly. In contrast, a person with a language disorder may have difficulty understanding what others are saying or expressing their thoughts and ideas in sentences.

Understanding the difference between these two concepts is essential for those in fields such as linguistics, communication studies, and speech-language pathology, as well as for anyone who wants to understand the complex nature of human communication better. It is important to note that early-interventionspeech-language pathologists target language and overall communication abilities. The rationale for not targeting speech sounds is that toddlers are just learning to understand and participate in the back-andforth of language and communication Speech sounds in American English do not all develop naturally until around age eight. That's when we would expect /s/, /v/, /th/, and /z/ to be naturally mastered. For a toddler with typically developing cognition and an adequately functioning oral cavity (mouth, lips, and tongue), we would expect to see the sounds of /m/ /b/ /p/ /h/ and /n/ to be produced accurately by age three.

Of course, there are always exceptions; if a child is deleting the initial sound of words, if they are distorting or having difficulty producing vowels, or if they are leaving out many of the sounds in words (they may only say a few consonant sounds) the SLP would likely choose to intervene before a child turns three.

CHAPTER 5

RECEPTIVE AND EXRESSIVE LANGUAGE

Receptive and expressive language refers to the two main ways people use language to communicate with others. Receptive language refers to the ability to understand and comprehend language. It includes understanding vocabulary, grammar, and the meaning of words, sentences, and conversations. People with good receptive language skills can follow instructions, understand conversations, and comprehend written and spoken
language.

Expressive language, on the other hand, refers to the ability to produce language and communicate effectively with others. Expressive language includes vocabulary, grammar, and the ability to effectively form coherent sentences and convey ideas. People with good expressive language skills can express their thoughts and ideas clearly, engage in conversation, and write well.

Receptive and expressive language are crucial for effective

communication However, a person with good receptive language skills may have difficulty expressing their thoughts effectively, while a person with strong expressive language skills may have trouble understanding others.

The human brain is an incredibly complex organ, and different parts of it are involved in various functions, including language use and understanding. Regarding language production, the brain's left hemisphere is primarily responsible for formulating and articulating words and sentences. The specific regions involved in language production include Broca's area, which is located in the frontal lobe, and the motor cortex, which controls the movements involved in speaking.

On the other hand, when it comes to language comprehension, multiple regions of the brain are involved. The temporal lobe, which is located on the side of the brain, plays a critical role in understanding spoken and written language. The Wernicke's area, located in the temporal lobe, is essential for understanding the meaning of words and sentences. The parietal lobe is also involved in language comprehension, as it processes information about word meanings and spatial relationships. Language use and understanding affect different brain parts but are closely interconnected and work together to allow us to communicate effectively.

Developing language skills in children typically begins with receptive language, which is commonly acquired before expressive language. Children first learn to understand language before they can use it themselves. As children grow and develop, they refine their receptive language skills and build their expressive language skills.

Language disorders can affect either receptive language, expressive language, or both. For example, children with receptive language disorders may have difficulty understanding language and following directions. In contrast, children with expressive language disorders may struggle with grammar, vocabulary, and the ability to form sentences.

Language disorders can significantly impact a person's ability to communicate effectively in personal and professional settings. Therefore, early diagnosis and treatment can be crucial in addressing language disorders and supporting individuals in developing the language skills they need to succeed.

Receptive and expressive language are the two main components of language and play a critical role in effective communication. While they are interdependent, they can also be impacted differently by language disorders, highlighting the importance of addressing both areas in language development and treatment.

Language processing disorder (LPD) differs from auditory processing disorder (APD). The latter is a condition in which the brain has difficulty processing and interpreting auditory information, despite normal hearing abilities. Difficulty in processing and interpreting can lead to difficulties in understanding speech in noisy environments, following verbal instructions, and retaining information

heard through auditory means. APD can impact learning, communication, and daily activities and is usually diagnosed through a series of tests by an audiologist.

CHAPTER 6

SIGN LANGUAGE

Sign language is a visual language with grammarand vocabulary, which can be used to communicate with people who are deaf, hard of hearing, or those who cannot speak. Hearing babies can also benefit from learning sign language, as it can help improve communication with their parents, caregivers, or other family members.

Advantages of teaching sign language to hearing babies:

1. **Improved Communication:** Sign language can be used as a tool for hearing babies to express their needs, wants, and fee ings before they can speak verbally.

2. **Reduced Frustration:** When a child cannot communicate their needs, it can lead to frustration and tantrums. Sign language can help reduce frustration by allowing babies to express themselves effectively.

3. **Enhanced Bonding:** When parents or caregivers use sign language with their hearing baby, it can create a unique bonding experience that strengthens the relationship between the parent and child.

4. **Improved Vocabulary:** Studies have shown that babies who learn sign language have a more extensive vocabulary and a better understanding of it than their peers who don't use sign language.

5. **Cognitive Development:** Signing with babies has been shown to positively affect their cognitive development, including improved problem-solving skills and increased creativity.

How to teach sign language to hearing babies:

1. **Start early:** The earlier a baby is exposed to sign language, the easier it is for them to learn. Some parents start teaching sign language to their babies as early as six months old.

2. **Use consistent signs:** It's essential to use consistent signs for common words, such as "eat," "drink," "milk," and "sleep." This consistency helps babies associate the sign with the word and understand the meaning of the sign.

3. **Use signs frequently:** Use signs frequently during everyday routines and activities, such as during mealtime, playtime, and bedtime.

4. **Model Signing:** Parents and caregivers should model signing for their babies and encourage them to imitate the signs.

5. **Make it Fun:** Make sign language a fun and interactive experience for the baby and the parent. Use silly signs, songs, and games to keep the baby engaged and excited about learning Teaching sign

language to hearing babies can provide numerous benefits, including improved communication, reduced frustration, enhanced bonding, improved vocabulary, and cognitive development. With consistency and patience, parents and caregivers can successfully teach their hearing babies sign language and provide them with a tool for communication that will last a lifetime.

Here are some tips for teaching sign language to toddlers:

1. **Start early:** Toddlers can start learning sign language as early as six months.

2. **Please keep it simple:** Use simple, easy-to-learn signs to start.

3. **Repeat, repeat, repeat:** Repetition is vital to help toddlers learn and remember signs.

4. **Use gestures:** Combine gestures with signs to reinforce the meaning.

5. **Use real-life situations:** Teach signs in context by using them in everyday situations.

6. **Make it fun:** Incorporate signs into playtime, songs, and stories.

7. **Use visual aids:** Use flashcards, videos, or books to help reinforce the signs.

8. **Practice regularly:** Consistently using signs will help solidify their learning.

9. **Encourage participation:** Encourage your toddler to imitate the signs and give them plenty of positive reinforcement

10. **Be patient:** Toddlers learn at their own pace, so be patient and don't pressure them.

11. **Make it a family affair:** Involve other family members in teaching and using sign language.

12. **Reinforce with spoken language:** As your toddler becomes more comfortable with signs, reinforce their learning by also using spoken language.

CHAPTER 7

AUGMENTATIVE AND ALTERNATIVE COMMUNICATION

Low-tech and high-tech Augmentative and Alternative Communication (AAC) devices are two approaches to helping people with communication difficulties. Low-tech AAC devices are simple, often manual, tools that aid communication. High-tech AAC devices are electronic and use advanced technology to support communication.

Low-tech AAC devices can include picture- or symbolbased communication boards, manual or electronic communication devices, and sign language. Picture- or symbol-based communication boards use images or symbols to represent words or phrases that can be pointed at or used in combination to express ideas. Manual communication devices include handing over small photos or pictures to convey messages.

Leading someone to the source of a desired object (juice, milk, water, etc.) is referred to as "prelinguistic." In order to teach a more advanced language skill, toddlers can learn to hand their parent a small photo or image of a sippy cup to indicate that they would like a drink. This action is referred to as "linguistic"; as the child can demonstrate their need or want for something without the item being present.

High-tech AAC devices are typically more sophisticated and are designed to support more complex communication needs. These devices can be divided into two categories: dedicated devices and mobile devices. Dedicated devices are standalone devices explicitly intended for communication and typically have a limited number of functions, such as text-tospeech synthesis, communication boards, and message banking. Mobile devices, such as smartphones and tablet computers, can be used as AAC devices, as they can run specialized software or apps that provide communication support.

Low-tech AAC devices have advantages over high-tech AAC, including being more affordable and accessible. In addition, they are often less dependent on technology and can be used in various settings. They also require less training to operate effectively and can be more reliable, as they are independent of batteries or
technology that can malfunction. One way a parent can encourage more communication is to offer the child a communication book that includes pages of symbols organized by topic that can be utilized to promote communication in various settings.

High-tech AAC has several advantages over low-tech devices, including being more flexible and providing a more comprehensive range of communication options. In addition, AAC can be customized to meet individual needs

and updated over time to reflect changing communication needs. High-tech AAC devices can also provide more opportunities for language development,
as they can store and recall messages and support literacy development.

In conclusion, low-tech and high-tech AAC devices have unique benefits and disadvantages. Low-tech devices are often more straightforward and reliable but may offer a different range of options than high-tech devices. High-tech devices are more sophisticated and provide greater flexibility, but they may also be more expensive and require more training to use effectively. The best AAC solution for individuals will depend on their needs, abilities, and preferences. With the guidance and recommendations of an SLP, parents, and students can try out different options over time before deciding which one will best suit the child's needs.

CHAPTER 8

PLAY IS PARAMOUNT

Play is a crucial aspect of language development in children. It allows children to explore their world, experiment with language, and practice communication skills. Through play, children develop their cognitive, social, and emotional abilities, which lays the foundation for effective communication.

One of the most critical aspects of play is its role in language development. Children learn language through interactions with others, and play provides a rich context for these interactions. Children are free to explore their language skills in a supportive and encouraging environment, which helps to build their confidence and self-esteem. Through play, children can experiment with different forms of language, such as gestures, sounds, and words, and learn the rules for how language is used in different situations. This process helps to build the child's cognitive and linguistic abilities, which are essential for future language development.

Another essential aspect of play is its role in developing social skills. Play provides children with opportunities to interact with others and practice their social skills, such as sharing, taking turns, and cooperating. These interactions help children to develop their emotional and social intelligence, which is essential for effective communication. In addition, children learn to understand and respond to others' emotions and perspectives, which is crucial for building relationships and interacting effectively with others.

In addition to its role in language and social development, play is also vital for children's physical development. Play provides children with opportunities to engage in physical activity, which helps to develop their fine and gross motor skills. This physical activity also supports the development of coordination, balance, and dexterity, which are essential for writing and other activities that require fine motor control.

Play is also essential for children's emotional development. Play allows children to express their emotions, explore them, and develop coping skills. Children can experiment with different ways of feeling and expressing emotions through play, which helps them to understand their own emotions and the emotions of others. This development is significant for children who may have difficulty expressing themselves verbally, as play provides them with a nonverbal outlet for their feelings.

Finally, play is vital for children's imaginative and creative development. Play provides children with opportunities to engage in innovative and creative activities, such as role-playing and make-believe. These activities help children to develop their imagination and creativity, which are essential for learning and problem-solving. In addition, children can experiment with different scenarios and perspectives, which helps them to develop their critical thinking skills and ability to understand complex ideas.

In conclusion, play is a critical component of language development in children. It allows children to explore their world, experiment with language, and practice communication skills. Through play, children develop their cognitive, social, emotional, and imaginative abilities, which lays the foundation for effective communication and future success. Parents and caregivers can support language development by encouraging children to engage in a variety of play experiences and by providing a supportive and encouraging environment for play and exploration.

Here are some fun toddler games/activities:

1. Simon Says game

2. Hokey-Pokey dance

3. Scavenger hunt

4. Obstacle course

5. Puzzles

6. Paint dot markers

7. Build a fort

8. Play I-spy

9. Play with stickers

10. Chalk drawings

CHAPTER 9

CHILDHOOD APRAXIA OF SPEECH

C hildhood apraxia of speech (CAS) is a neurodevelopmental disorder that affects a child's ability to produce speech sounds accurately. The causes of CAS are not well understood, but research suggests a combination of genetic and environmental factors may play a role.

One theory is that CAS may be caused by damage to the nerve pathways that control the muscles used for speech, or by problems with the brain's ability to plan and coordinate the movements needed for speech. Other factors contributing to the development of CAS include premature birth, low birth weight, brain injury, and neurological conditions such as cerebral palsy or autism spectrum disorder.

The symptoms of CAS can vary but typically include difficulty with speech sound production, poor intelligibility, and a struggle to coordinate the movements needed for speech. Children with CAS may also have trouble with oral motor skills, such as chewing and swallowing.

Treatment for CAS is typically delivered by a speechlanguage pathologist, who will work with the child to develop their speech and communication skills. The approach to treatment will depend on the individual child's needs. Still, some common strategies include the following:

1. **Speech Therapy:** Speech therapy will focus on helping the child to produce speech sounds correctly, improve their speech intelligibility, and develop their oral motor skills.

2. **Augmentative and Alternative Communication (AAC):** If a child has difficulty communicating verbally, AAC may be a supplement or alternative to speech. This alternative communication could include sign language, picture symbols, or communication devices.

3. **Speech-Generating Devices:** These are specialized devices that can be programmed to produce speech for the child. They may be helpful for children with severe speech difficulties who cannot communicate effectively through other means.

4. **Articulation Therapy:** This therapy focuses on teaching the child to produce specific speech sounds correctly and may include exercises such as repetition and shaping.

5. **Fluency Therapy:** If the child has a stuttering problem, fluency therapy may help them improve their fluency and reduce their stuttering.

6. **Oral-Motor Therapy:** This therapy focuses on strengthening the muscles used for speech and improving the child's oral motor control.

7. **PROMPT©**: Stands for Prompts for Restructuring Oral Muscular Phonetic Targets. It is a speech therapy technique that uses prompts or cues to help children improve their speech skills. For example, the therapist may use verbal cues, gestures, or visual aids to prompt the person to produce the correct sounds, words, or sentences. The techniques aim to help the individual become more independent in communication by gradually reducing the need for prompts over time. To be certified in this method, a speech-language pathologist attends PROMPT© training courses and meets several certification requirements established by the PROMPT© Institute.

In addition to these treatment options, parents and caregivers must provide a supportive and encouraging environment for the child. This support may include working with the child at home on their speech and communication skills, encouraging them to participate in social activities, and seeking support from other families in similar situations.

In conclusion, while the causes of CAS are not fully understood, early diagnosis and treatment are essential for improving a child's communication ability. With the proper support and therapy, children with CAS can make significant progress in their speech and language development.

CHAPTER 10

SENSORY INTEGRAT ION

Some kids are hard to figure out. We may see they are unhappy, frightened, or moody, but we may not always be able to determine the cause. The nervous system is responsible for transmitting signals between the brain and the body. When the nervous system is stressed, the body feels dysregulated. As a result, susceptible children may have trouble processing sensory information. When a child struggles with a sensory processing disorder, their daily behavior can be challenging, and their speech acquisition can also be impaired.

Sensory Processing Disorder (SPD) is a neurodevelopmental condition that affects how individuals process and integrate sensory information from their environment. The condition can impact individuals in different ways and to varying degrees, making it challenging to diagnose and treat.

SPD is often characterized by difficulties processing sensory information from one or more categories: touch, sound, sight, taste, smell, movement (vestibular), and body position (proprioception). For example, a person with SPD may have trouble tolerating loud noises, the textures of certain foods, or the feel of clothing. Some individuals with SPD may seek sensory stimulation, such as crashing into things or jumping excessively. In contrast, others may avoid sensory stimuli, such as not wanting to wear certain clothes or avoiding certain activities.

Diagnosis of SPD can be complex, as no medical tests can determine the disorder's presence. Instead, a comprehensive evaluation involves a combination of medical, developmental, and psychological assessments to rule out other conditions and determine the presence of sensory processing difficulties.

Treatment for SPD typically involves a multi-disciplinary approach, including occupational therapy (OT), speech therapy, and behavioral therapy. OT is the most commonly used treatment for SPD. It focuses on helping individuals with the disorder develop the skills they need to engage in daily activities and improve their quality of life. In addition, OT interventions may include sensory integration therapy, which involves engaging in activities designed to help the individual better process and respond to sensory information.

In addition to therapy, some strategies and accommodations can help individuals with SPD manage their symptoms. These may include changes to the individual's environment, such as reducing or modifying sensory stimuli or using adaptive equipment to help with daily activities. It may also involve modifying behavior, such as teaching coping skills to manage sensory sensitivities or avoiding specific triggers.

What is the difference between a tantrum and a meltdown?

When kids have tantrums, they are aware of what's going on around them. As a result, the tantrum is controlled and purposeful, and the child is frustrated and communicating through the tantrum. In contrast, a meltdown is when the child is highly emotional, dysregulated, overwhelmed, and is not responsive to attempts to get them to snap out of it.

Some signs your child is experiencing sensory overload can include:

1. Covering ears
2. Squinting eyes / blinking / covering eyes
3. Touching everything
4. Bumping into people or things
5. Running inside and outside the home
6. Jumping on the furniture
7. Rolling around on the carpet or floor
8. Putting everything in their mouth/chewing
9. Complaining things sound very loud
10. Producing loud sounds/noise
11. Tapping/banging things

It is crucial to determine what triggers a child to help them regulate their nervous system. First, parents can attempt to figure out what the triggers are. Then it may become clearer whether they need more or less sensory input. Parents need to be flexible in deciding which activities to try, and they should keep an open mind about how the child responds to the change. Remember to consider all the senses, including sight, sound, touch, taste, and smell. Other senses include: vestibular (balance), interoception (the body's sense of its internal organs, hunger, thirst, temperature, bladder, and bowel sensations), and proprioception (which tells us where our body parts are without having to look for them).Proprioception helps us to know where body parts are relative to each other, strengthening our coordination skills. It also tells us how much force to use when holding, pushing, pulling, or lifting objects.

Sensory Processing Disorder (SPD) can affect speech and language development in various ways. Children with SPD may have difficulties processing sensory information, including auditory and visual information, leading to problems with attention, focus, and memory. SPD can result in difficulties with listening and following instructions, which are crucial for developing speech and language skills. Additionally, children with SPD may experience challenges with oral motor skills, such as coordinating the movements of the mouth and tongue, which can impact speech intelligibility. However, it's important to note that every child with SPD may not have speech and language difficulties and that each case is unique. An evaluation by a speechlanguage pathologist and occupational therapist can help determine the impact of SPD on speech and language development.

CONCLUSION

Ultimately, knowing how to help kids who are not speaking or have limited speech is neither easy noz straightforward. There isn't a simple recipe or how-to manual for teaching kids to communicate. The urge to compare our children to other children is common.

However, it is essential to understand that not all children develop speech at the same pace. Various factors can contribute to a child being a late talker, such as hearing loss, developmental delays, or simply a slower pace of language development.

If you suspect your child may be a late talker, it is essential to consult a pediatrician or speech-language pathologist. They can assess the root cause and provide recommendations for speech therapy and other interventions to help your child catch up. It is also essential to continue to provide a language-rich environment for your child through reading, storytelling, and conversing with them, even if they are not yet speaking.

Research has shown that early intervention is crucial for late-talking children, and with proper support, many of them can catch up and reach their language milestones. However, it is also essential to have realistic expectations, as some children may have persistent speech difficulties and may need ongoing support.

Nevertheless, with patience, persistence, and the proper support, some of the most late-talking children can develop strong communication skills and go on to lead successful and fulfilling lives.

Give
Them
The
Words

Improving Communication for Exceptional Kids:
•Feelings •Emotions •Learning Styles
•Self-Awareness •Parental Guidance

Kim Gallo M.S., CCC-SLP

Introduction

Have you ever had a word stuck at the tip of your tongue something that makes perfect sense in your head but little to those around you? Or have you had this happen to someone you know? For me, it's safe to say that I've experienced both. From being flustered enough to only mouth "uhs" and "ahs" to being presented with children who would do the same.

Words are our tools of communication, but sometimes learning to use those tools effectively can be difficult for both children and adults. Development of language takes place at different times, and so does the correct use of language, irrespective of whether a child is neurotypical or neurodiverse. Having said that, children can display differences when it comes to learning and then using language. Struggling to convey one's feelings accurately can be a frustrating exercise, and this book addresses those hurdles specifically.

This book was written to break these barriers, to topple the wall between those who look for semblance and those able to provide, and to give insight into the many experiences of neurodivergent children and adolescents from a speech pathologist's point of view. Not only will this book provide you with information regarding the importance and effectiveness of words, but it will also broaden your mind on the very subject.

There is likely a selection of books available for you to choose from, so why pick mine? It is fair to claim that I have inside experience when it comes to dealing with neurodivergent children and adolescents—especially ones that find it hard to use their words. While earning a bachelor's degree in psychology in the late '90s, I worked alongside certified Behavior Analysts teaching young toddlers who were newly diagnosed with Autism. I then earned a BCaBA (Board Certified Associate Behavior Analyst Certification) in 2002 and a master's degree in Speech-Language Pathology (SLP) in 2004. In 2005, I earned my Certificate of Clinical Competence (CCC) and became Certified by the American Speech and Hearing Association (ASHA). I have worked in Early Intervention and K-12 schools, as well as in private practice with both children and young adults. I am the parent of two, one of which is a neurodivergent young adult.

I will take you on a journey into the world of communication. Neurodivergent individuals can have difficulties expressing themselves, which becomes frustrating. However, when taught how to do so, they can reach a point where they feel less overwhelmed and less restricted. Feelings go hand in hand with words in that without a word to attach to a feeling, communication is pretty challenging. Activities engaging our senses are also useful, as well as forms of non-verbal communication that can be transformed into conversations.

On the subject of senses, we will look at all eight of them. Yes, there are eight, which open the door to sensory overload, which I will explain in detail. One has to remember that autistic children respond differently to sensory activation. For instance, one child may be very fond of loud music, whereas another will find loud music uncomfortable and anxiety-inducing. The same goes for touch and the other senses. You will learn the differences, and the concept of dysregulation, which amounts to being out of sync and displaying either high or low levels of arousal. The next section is a lesson on managing situations to facilitate regulation. This section will include the zones of regulation model, which classifies sensory experiences and movement between zones.

Communication is divided into eight categories, much like the senses, but the difference is that the categories are back-and-forth stepping stones used when communicating. Think of it like tennis; there is back and forth, but not always the same shot. The struggles that autistic children have within the categories are highlighted, and as parents or teachers of autistic children, you will identify.

I will also take you through the different styles of language learning, as a detailed breakdown, and give you exercises that suit verbal learners or natural learners, for instance. As with anyone, some children prefer learning in groups, while others favor individual learning. This concept is explored, along with the concepts of Gestalt and analytical language learners, followed by a detailed section on echolalia, which is the repetition of words without context. This is a particularly interesting trait for some children, and I will show you some exercises that can be done to create context and improve on using words correctly in a situation.

Sign language as a tool to work towards understanding how to build communication skills that become verbal will be explained, as well as methods involving devices like manual communication boards and voice output records, among others.

There will be detailed information on Early Intervention (EI) programs and the legislation that provides for equal education opportunities. Education is not restricted to school, and I will show you how to set up your home and how to interact with your child and the rest of the family. As a parent of an neurodivergent child, I understand the challenges that parents face, which are elaborated on. In addition, I will explain some methods of mitigating the stress involved in raising children, autistic or not.

I have included some stories from parents of autistic children, transcribed directly from videos, that readers will identify with. It is always good to know that there are others with which you can empathize, and this section is a great reminder of that. Emotional support structures are touched on, and I explain the ways in which parents can manage the transition into adolescence. One of the ways is to build self-esteem in our children and to let them know that neurodiversity is a strength.

We all have differences in opinion about social media, but I think we can agree that teenagers love it. This does not mean that using social media is free of its problems. You will find some statistics and recommendations based thereon as to limited screen time and social media use in general.

I finish off with non-verbal autism, including augmentative and alternative communication systems, strategies, and tools. Visual displays such as charts and social stories are discussed, as well as the development of emotional intelligence. When you reach the end of your read, you will have a broader understanding of just how and why words are so essential. Rest assured, it is safe to say that you'll be able to "give them the words."

Chapter 1

Words and Feelings

"Sticks and stones might break my bones, but words will never hurt me." This is an idiom that nobody really knows the origin of. However, unless you are a psychopath, you know that it is not true!

Words

One of the definitions, according to Merriam-Webster's dictionary, is "a speech sound or series of speech sounds that symbolizes and communicates a meaning usually without being divisible into smaller units capable of independent use" (Merriam-Webster, n.d.). Words are important because they allow us to communicate our thoughts and feelings. Words can be spoken, written, or read. Words are powerful because they have the ability to make things happen. We use words to inform, confirm, deny, protest, negate, and question. Words are symbols that represent things and can also be represented visually, such as in drawings or photographs.

We can do so much with our words. Words provide affirmations of our thoughts. Words are powerful and can be used to cause pain or warm hearts. One single word can cause tremendous pain or give us hope. Words can also be empty. Have you ever had a conversation with someone who continues to talk incessantly regardless of whether you look or seem interested? They keep talking even when you are attempting to indicate that you are not following the story. Words can be deceptive. Misleading words, more commonly known as lies, are often spoken for a variety of reasons, such as to avoid punishment, to protect ourselves, to maintain our privacy, or to avoid embarrassment.

Words can be clues that are used to predict behavior. Words tell us a lot about one's character if we listen carefully. Words allow us to show how innovative, creative, and intelligent our minds can be. They can inspire and change our lives. Mental health workers, counselors, and teachers are just some professions with such immense power. A simple conversation with them can change a life forever.

On the other hand, negative, hurtful words impact people on a physical level. Has anyone ever used words that made you feel like you've been physically punched or stabbed? We must remember here that, of course, we cannot control what comes out of other people's minds and mouths, but we can choose to think about them in a way that leaves us feeling less wounded.

When we hear words from specific sources, it is natural for us to believe those words. Words spoken by familiar sources hold even more true when we hear the exact words repeatedly. Marketers and advertisers know that if you are exposed to a message frequently, you are more likely to believe it even when it contains a non-fact. People with low self-esteem often have low self-esteem because they've lived in a world created by someone else's words. One of the top thinkers on the future of culture, relevance, and the internet is Gary Vaynerchuk; he says:

"The number one way to protect a child is to build their self-esteem. When a child is not insecure, they don't succumb to danger" (Vaynerchuk, 2022). By using the right words, we can accomplish this.

As a Speech-Language Pathologist who works in a school setting with teens, I often have students come to my office for their therapy time. A while ago, I had a student come in, and while we were making our initial small talk, I noticed that he had an odd look. Initially, I just asked him if everything was okay, and he responded by saying, "I'm fine," but as I continued to talk, I felt like his face was trying to tell me something. I stopped talking and said to him, "Aiden (not his real name), I can tell by looking at your face that something is bothering you. Please tell me what's bothering you?" Initially, he said, "I feel like my brain is on crack." Still unclear on what that meant, I proceeded to ask him several more questions. He explained to me that there was a substitute teacher in the class that he had just come from. I was aware that youngsters in many schools don't always act in an appropriate manner when a replacement teacher is there. This substitute teacher was given a lesson plan and attempted to implement it. Unfortunately, the students had other ideas. Aiden explained that they were rambunctious, rowdy, and loud. They were out of their seats and ignored all the teacher's requests to sit and attend

the lesson. Aiden was especially appalled
that this adult female teacher could somehow tune out or
ignore what she was witnessing. The substitute stood in
front of the class and continued to try to teach the lesson
even though only a handful of students were actually
listening and ready to learn.

Aiden is a kind and thoughtful child. He is a diligent
student and a conscientious worker. He is also Autistic.
He and I proceeded to talk about what was happening
inside of him while he was witnessing this madness. He
explained to me, after a lot of coaxing, that at first, he was
feeling a bit bothered, but it quickly turned into feeling
confused and agitated about being in that classroom. He
said, "My heart was beating fast for no reason, and I felt
a little dizzy."

This child is an honor student with straight A's who
receives positive teacher praise and prides himself in doing
the right thing. He has friends and belongs to some of the
school clubs. So, how could a child of his academic caliber
and good senses not find the words to describe what he
was experiencing during that class? And why didn't he just
ask to be excused so he could get some air and relax? He
didn't have the words.

I spent the rest of the session giving him the words.

Feelings

Learning to recognize our own thoughts and emotions
is a skill that is crucial for children and adults to develop
in order to be fully present in our lives. When we are

unable to recognize our thoughts and feelings, it can lead to a wide range of behaviors, some of which may or may not be beneficial to our health. Abuse of substances like drugs and alcohol are common Band-aids used to alleviate suffering. The illusion of comfort can also be created by addictions such as compulsive overeating, gambling, or excessive exercise. Some people have the good fortune to discover more constructive strategies to deal with unsettling feelings. For instance, activities involving some form of art, such as dance or painting, provide a more constructive outlet for coping with uncomfortable feelings.

Whenever I consider how vital it is to pin down my emotions, music is the first thing that comes to me. If songwriters are confronted with powerful and overpowering sensations, they express those emotions through the lyrics of the songs they write. People have a lot on their plates because life can be difficult. Unanticipated events can occur at any time, and how we feel about them and how we respond to them are important factors in determining whether, how, when, and where we progress. When everything in the life of a healthy and balanced individual is going well, recognizing one's emotional space does not provide much of a challenge. We make it a habit to check in with ourselves periodically to ascertain how we feel and what we might require. Talking to someone who works in the field of mental health professions and who has received specialized training is a different experience than having that conversation with one of your closest friends or relatives. They utilize a variety of methods that will enable you to investigate your past and get a glimpse into your unconscious mind.

Regrettably, not everyone possesses the expertise, access, or finances necessary to collaborate with professionals such as these. Without a trained professional, such as a psychologist, how can you learn to recognize your feelings, find a solution to a problem, pull yourself out of a state of depression, or mend a broken relationship?

Dr. Joan Cusack Handler, author of the book "Identifying Your Feelings," is a psychologist and researcher. According to an article published in Psychology Today, we should "Start by taking our emotional temperature." She challenges us to identify the sensations that we are currently conscious of (Agnionline, n.d.). Which of the five senses predominates the most? And at what point did we first become conscious of the sensation? Next, what factors might contribute to producing this sensation? What is taking place in our everyday lives, and what is not taking place? If, at that time, we are unable to determine how we are feeling, she proposes that we evaluate our conduct and everyday life by questioning our home life, relationship with a partner, children, parents, and siblings, and other aspects of these relationships. Can you fill us in on the situation at work? Is one able to have fun there? Is everything all right with the manager? After you have provided your responses to these questions, you should consider the veracity of the answers you have provided. When you acknowledge an emotion, you can better understand what you're experiencing and why. It is also a test of how effectively you can understand the thoughts and feelings of other people. Having a skill as priceless and valuable as this one is hard to come by.

The majority of human communication is done through non-verbal means. It is essential to not only pay attention to the words being said but also be aware of what you may be seeing, as nonverbal cues such as facial expressions, vocal tone, and body language can frequently reveal how a person is feeling. It is essential for us to be human so that we are able to comprehend our own ideas and feelings (versus animals). When we have an understanding of our own thoughts and feelings, it will be easier for us to articulate why we feel the way we do and to empathize with the emotions that others are experiencing.

When we are able to verbally convey our thoughts, feelings, and experiences in the form of language, we are able to fulfill not just our own needs but also the needs of those around us. Your capacity to deal with an emotion is improved simply by being able to put a name to what you are experiencing and how you are feeling. The more words we provide children to describe their feelings and emotions, the more likely it is that they will acquire those words and be able to assimilate the important life lesson that it is highly beneficial and empowering to communicate our feelings and emotions. Because doing so requires a certain degree of openness and vulnerability, putting one's thoughts and feelings into words can be a challenging task.

We demonstrate our emotional intelligence and awareness when we are able to comprehend and think about how others feel, as well as when we are able to understand and think about how we ourselves feel. If we put that knowledge and attention to work to solve problems and take control of our feelings, we will be able to assist others in doing the same. Putting a name to an emotion makes it easier to manage and come to terms with that sensation.

One of the many meanings of the word "regulate" is "the ability to govern something, particularly by causing it to function in a predetermined manner," which can be found in the dictionary published by Merriam-Webster. There are many different kinds of regulations, and one of them is the regulation of emotions. This refers to our capacity to translate how we are feeling and what we are thinking into behaviors that are appropriate for the context in which we find ourselves. A person who possesses a high level of emotional intelligence has the ability to lessen the impact of strong feelings. They have the ability to adjust and reduce their levels of rage and anxiety.

The way one thinks has the power to alter the tone of what a person is feeling on the inside as well as on the outer. Even while most people are familiar with terms such as mad, sad, happy, excited, and angry, there are literally hundreds of more words that can be used to express feelings and emotions. Marc Brackett, the founder of the Yale Centre for Emotional Intelligence and influential psychologist, authored a book called Permission to Feel, in which he writes, "being able to communicate words such as shame, guilt, humiliation, jealousy, envy, joy, contentment, stress, and pressure displays some of the greatest levels of what is known as emotional intelligence" (Rabbitt, 2022). Think about how much more specific you are as a communicator when you describe someone or something by using terms like fulfilled, harmonic, and invigorated.

Chapter 2

The Eight Senses and Why They Really Matter

Our sensory system helps us get information about the world around us. The senses help us stay alive and well. They help us in everyday life, like playing sports, driving, or navigating an unfamiliar place. The senses help us when listening to a tune or enjoying a meal. The senses allow us to have enjoyable experiences. Our feelings, emotions, and memories are quite connected with the senses.

Looking back at my University days, training as a Speech-Language Pathologist in the early 2000s, I don't remember the sensory system being mentioned in the way I have come to know it.

In 2005, I began working on a multidisciplinary team of pediatric therapists. While there, I was introduced to play therapists, feeding specialists, and physical and occupational therapists. Some of these men and women would be working with the same children I was assigned to treat for a speech or language delay, difference, or disorder.

At this facility, working among these professionals, I gained substantial insight and knowledge about the senses. When working with children under age six, I sometimes used a small, child-size table and chairs in my office when I wasn't sitting on the floor or using the playroom. One day, when working with a student, the Occupational Therapist (OT) walked into my workspace to grab a book. She looked at me and asked me, "Why are her feet dangling like that?" I thought the chair was small enough for a child under age six. Admittedly, it was slightly bigger than I'd like-but, just slightly more prominent. I looked up at the OT, feeling quite confused, not knowing what to say. Finally, she said, "You should put her feet up on some sort of box." Still confused and clueless, I replied, "I'm working on her speech development; what do her feet being on a box have to do with her ability to produce speech and language?." She answered my question, and I was intrigued by her unexpected and thorough answer. This was the start of MY Special Education as an SLP. For the next five years, I worked side-by-side with the "Dream Team." These were some of the kindest, most caring, and most intelligent women in the field. Together, we co-treated children while educating each other about the knowledge we had specific to our disciplines.

The most valuable lesson I have learned from this team is that all behavior is communication. I learned that most symptoms of behaviors we see in our children start in the nervous system. Admittedly, upon first hearing it, the terminology used by these therapists sounded "hokey" to me. They used all kinds of words and phrases I was unfamiliar with to explain things I perceived as moodiness, tantrums, or non-compliance. Several words I heard regularly that initially didn't make sense to me. Words like

REGULATE, SENSORY DIET, VESTIBULAR INPUT, AND POOR PROPRIOCEPTION PROCESSING...

What the heck kind of language was this? As I stated previously, this was the education I never knew I wanted, but I quickly realized it was the education I needed. And I didn't need it just to work with my Speech and Language students; I needed it for myself and my own child, who, luckily, was young enough at the time to benefit from all this crucial information. In order to explain what I've learned, I will start by building on some of the knowledge you most likely already have. We formally learn the

basics of the five senses as young as kindergarten. By the time we get to a high school anatomy class, we can have a pretty detailed understanding of it. To refresh the memory of those who may have forgotten, the five senses are:

1. **Olfactory/Smell:** How something smells can help us know about the world. Smell is one of the principal ways we interact with the environment. Our sense of smell can be valuable in determining whether the milk is spoiled, or you are tracking dog feces throughout the house on the bottom of your shoe.

2. **Vision/Sight Perception:** Our eyes give us vital information about the world. Our sense of vision helps us see things that are near and far. It helps us to detect light and color via the cells in the retina at the

back of the eye.

3. **Taste/Gustatory:** Our tongue receives taste sensations and determines if the sensation is harmful. What we think about the flavor depends on combining our senses of taste, smell, and touch. The combination of these things determines whether we like the taste of food.

4. **Touch/Tactile:** There are nerve endings and touch receptors in the skin; this allows us to feel different textures, temperatures, and pain, which is necessary for avoiding injury.

5. **Hearing/Auditory:** The mechanical sense of hearing works by turning physical movement into electrical signals, which get translated into vibrations, and we experience those vibrations as sounds.

There are three more senses that are super significant. They are what I like to call the VIP Systems because they are Very Important Parts. They are as follows:

• Vestibular Sense controls your balance and knowledge of where your body is in space.

• Interoception is awareness of the body's physical signs and symptoms. It is what's happening inside the body and our attention to it. Are we hungry? Are we thirsty? Do we have to urinate or have a bowel movement? Are we feeling chilly or too hot?

• Proprioception Processing - this is the body's ability to sense itself. The body can vary how muscles, tendons, and joints respond to incoming information regarding outside forces.

Before I go on, I'd like to define a few words or terms that will hopefully help you understand what took me a while to figure out.

First, the Nervous system is the command center of the body (so it's super important that it works appropriately). It has four parts, as follows:

- The Central Nervous System (CNS): The brain and the spinal cord

- The Peripheral Nervous System (PNS): The nerves that connect the brain and spinal cord to the peripheral nervous system, which is what nerve tissue outside of the central nervous system is called.

- Somatic Nervous System (SNS): Also part of the peripheral nervous system. One of its roles is to relay information we see, hear, and feel to the brain. It is responsible for the voluntary control of body movements. So, when we are thinking about walking, the SNS takes that thought, sends it to the muscles in our legs, and makes it happen. When someone has a spinal cord injury, the messages cannot travel from the brain to the body. The spinal nerves below the injury level receive the signal but cannot travel up the spinal tract to the brain. One might continue to have reflex movements, but they are not purposeful or controllable.

- The Autonomic System (ANS): One of the primary functions of the peripheral nervous system's autonomic nervous system, which controls glands and organs without the intervention of our conscious minds, is to maintain bodily functions.

Sympathetic and Parasympathetic Systems

These systems work together to coordinate the changes that our bodies require to function throughout the environment. For example, the pupils in our eyes adjust in size according to the light present to give us the best vision. Likewise, when the temperature gets hot, our sweat glands are turned on to regulate our body's internal temperature.

I like to think of the word regulate as regular. When you feel regular, you feel okay; you are not agitated or annoyed; you are not hot or hungry. When we hear the word sensory, just know we are referring to one of the senses. The term sensory dysregulation is used to describe someone whose body is over or under-reacting to the incoming sensory information. We would then say that that person is poorly regulated.

What Does Poor Regulation Look Like? And What Kinds of Things Can Make Someone Dysregulated?

It can look like whining, tantrums, fussing, unsettled, highly emotional, or moody. The term level of arousal can be defined by how near or far a person is from being regular… oops, I meant regulated. Our ability to control our level of arousal is called self-regulation.

In a case of low arousal levels, it can look like the person is tired, lazy, or distracted. For example, a child may slump in their chair, need to prop their head up with their hands and become easily distracted by other sensory input in the room.

Children subject to high-level arousal may be in constant motion or appear agitated or disorganized. For example, a child may be bouncing, constantly getting out of their chair, climbing, or moving heavy objects around (like the sofa).

How Can an Adult, Parent, or Child Change the Arousal Level?

Sensory modulation: Helping and advising people to control their emotional state by employing their senses, such as sight, sound, smell, touch, taste, and movement. Some tools that can be used as examples are music, essential oils, rocking chairs, weighted items, and massage chairs. An optimum level of arousal is reached when the information your senses take in is tolerable and allows you to function well.

What Does This Look Like in an Actual Situation Regarding a Child?

Jayden is a 7-year-old 1st-grade student at Mariner Elementary School. He loves wearing sweatpants because they are soft and comfortable. He wakes up one morning and begins getting ready for the day. Unfortunately, his mom got behind on the laundry, so the only clean thing he can wear is jeans. So, his mom helps him put on the jeans while he attempts to wiggle away from her. Because of the jeans, Jayden's nervous system is activated. Jayden goes downstairs to eat breakfast. Mom serves Rice Krispies versus the Corn Flakes that Jayden usually prefers. He has some oral hypersensitivity, which causes him to choose a dry crunchy texture versus a soft mushy one. When the milk hits the Krispies, they get way too soggy. Now Jayden is getting even more dysregulated. Mom can't drive Jayden to school that day because she has an appointment, so she asks Pam, the neighbor, to take him. Unfortunately for Jayden, neighbor Pam has two 4th-grade rambunctious twins, and Jayden has a sensitive hearing auditory system. Now he's on his way to school, and the other children are playing around. The twins are inadvertently touching him, and their voices are loud. This adds another couple of notches to his already dysregulated nervous system. He finally arrives at school, and another child takes off his backpack, and his arm accidentally touches Jayden's shoulder. Jayden loses the ability to control himself and punches the child. His school day hasn't even started, and he is already at the top of the chart with every sensory event that challenges his nervous system. This sensory overload or high dysregulation activated his sympathetic nervous system and pushed him into a fight, flight, or freeze mode. While there are several techniques to de-escalate this response, prevention of the build-up of several sensory events is what's ideal.

As educators, we must do all that we can to prevent this from happening to our children because, over time, the consequences of this chronic stress can lead to other mental and physical problems, such as anxiety and depression, as well as physical challenges such as high blood pressure and hair loss.

As a parent, addressing your own nervous system is important because mirror neurons fire when we are experiencing something and when we witness someone experiencing something. Our children are mirroring our nervous system, and we are mirroring their nervous system. So, parents have to learn how to REGULATE their own nervous system so they can be in an ideal position to help their children.

Sensory Dysregulation in More Detail

According to Sydney Thorson, OT, "sensory dysregulation refers to a mind or body state which occurs when the body is out of balance due to experiences in the sensory environment" (Thorson, 2022). When we experience things through our senses, those stimuli make us feel a certain way. My tolerance for music at volume 10 is different from my son's. I have tolerance for the tag on my shirt-my daughter will lose her mind if it touches her neck and back. I can eat lunch at a table with my peers; a co-worker, Mr. Jones, smells my yogurt and begins to gag. Sensory dysregulation happens when the body's nervous system perceives too much or too little stimulation for best functioning, and self-regulation is not naturally occurring. I had a toddler-age student years ago when I was working for Early Intervention, whose body was always in motion. He had a strong, solid build. He was an agile climber and was quite tolerant of pain. He rarely cried when he had a fall that resulted in him being bruised or bloodied. He stuffed large quantities of food in his mouth when self-feeding. His mother was often worried he would choke. After working with the "Dream Team," I knew this child was a sensory seeker. His nervous system was understimulated, so his body spent much of its time seeking ways to self-regulate.

Everyone's nervous system is different. Everyone's ability to self-regulate is also different. When you are in tune with what your body needs when something is too much or too little, you can simply adjust your choices or the environment. Sometimes our children present undesired behaviors that we often don't understand. There is a strong possibility that the issue may be stemming from their nervous system.

Contrary to what many people believe, your child will not grow out of their sensory issues. No amount of discipline will change how a child's body feels when it's not regulated. Children often act out because they feel overwhelmed or unsafe. Things like timeouts and punishment do not improve those conditions. If your child climbs all over the furniture and jumps on their bed, it could be happening because their sensory system requires an increased need for movement. If your child is clingy and it seems as though they have to touch everything in the environment, they may be struggling with body awareness and may not even realize exactly where their body is in relation to yours.

Simply put, when the nervous system isn't balanced, it can be due to a condition called Sensory Processing Disorder (SPD). Children and adults with SPD feel dysregulated more often than neurotypicals. Without intervention, they have far less ability to self-regulate. While SPDs can exist in isolation, they may be most prevalent in those with Autism Spectrum or Attention Deficit Disorders.

How can we help? How can Jayden's before-school scenario look brighter moving forward? When children are struggling to modulate their senses, and as a result, negative consequences occur. I recommend consulting an occupational therapist or developmental pediatrician. First, as parents, we can learn to track the triggers. We need to explore how different sensations make our children feel. Certain places, bright light, loud noises, and not knowing what will happen next are all things that can be too much or not enough for some children. Getting wet, getting dirty, going for car rides, being interrupted while talking, or making a mistake can also produce an unexpected response from a child. After experiencing some of the circumstances I just mentioned, it can make a child feel anywhere in the range between feeling nothing at all or they may feel unbearable. Some signs that your child may be experiencing sensory overload include touching everything, running or pacing, jumping on the furniture, covering their ears, squinting their eyes are blinking, rolling on the floor, making noises, often complaining that things are too loud, too bright too tight, chewing on things that are not necessarily edible, and poor eye contact. In the case of Jayden, he was experiencing higher and higher levels of arousal as the morning progressed. When he got to school, his nervous system was overloaded, and he lost control. He would benefit from an occupational therapy evaluation and treatment plan.

Occupational therapists often recommend "sensory diets"

to children with self-regulation challenges. The term "diet" initially confused me because I associate the word diet with food. However, a sensory diet is not necessarily about food. It is more like a plan, recommended to regulate (calm or arouse) depending on the affected senses. We must be willing to experiment and make changes.

We can use devices in each sensory-system category to stimulate or calm the nervous system. The same device, such as a swing, may calm one child and may trigger another child. The tool can have no effect at all, or it can relax, excite, or trigger. Here are some explanations and examples:

Touch/Tactile

Sensory seekers crave touch, generally have a high tolerance for pain, and often get messy. Sensory avoiders avoid touch, prefer certain textures, are very neat, and start away from crowds. The following sensory supporting devices can be used:

- bins filled with rice

- weighted blankets and vests

- firm squeezes

- playdough moon sand

Sight/Visual

Seekers will stare at ceiling fans or lights, hold items very close to their eyes, and lose their places while reading. Avoiders dislike bright light, struggle with eye contact, and are startled easily. The following sensory supporting devices can be used:

- light table

- lava lamps or something similar

- marbles

Hearing/Auditory

Seekers tend to make loud noises, have the TV volume up high, and use such to feel calm. Avoiders don't like crowds, will often be seen covering their ears, and do not like everyday sounds (blender or a flushing toilet). The following sensory supporting devices can be used:

- quiet space

- earplugs or headphones

- calming music

- learning a musical instrument

Taste/Oral

Seekers enjoy strong tastes like spicy foods and will often

chew on non-edibles. Avoiders stay away from certain textures of foods and are very restricted in what they eat, and may find it difficult to use some utensils (knives, forks, cups, straws). The following sensory supporting devices can be used:

- chewing gum or eating candy

- chewable toys or jewelry

- blowing whistles, horns, and bubbles

- trying new foods

- trying utensils made of novel materials

- using a vibrating toothbrush

Smell/Olfactory

Seekers tend to smell objects but also people. They find strong smells appealing and actively seek them out. Avoiders can find ordinarily pleasant smells very unpleasant. The following sensory supporting devices can be used:

- scented toys or playdough

- aromatherapy

- perfumes or cologne

- strongly scented objects stored away

Vestibular

The vestibular system doesn't affect seeking and avoiding behavior but rather affects spatial awareness, coordination, and balance. Sport, especially involving a ball, has shown to be effective in improving the aforesaid skills. The following sensory supporting devices can be used:

- swinging

- bike riding

- swimming

- playing catch

- kicking a soccer ball

Interoception

Interoception allows individuals to perceive the internal state of their own body, including sensations such as hunger, thirst, heart rate, breathing rate, and temperature interoception plays a critical role in regulating the body's internal processes and maintaining homeostasis and is also thought to be involved in emotional and social cognition, as well as decision-making and self-awareness. Individuals with impaired interoception may experience difficulties in recognizing and responding to their own bodily needs and emotions.

The interception system struggles to provide an identification of cold, warmth, thirst, or hunger. Teaching children about their bodies improves awareness of what they are experiencing. The best way to do so is to increase awareness by saying something such as, "It's been four to five hours since you last ate something. You are likely feeling hungry." Then have the child gain awareness of how they are feeling at that moment. This is a complicated sense, and for those who struggle with it, a more systematic guide may be required. In the interoception curriculum, author Kelly Mahler outlines an approach professionals can use to teach parents and clients.

Proprioception

Proprioception is the sense that allows individuals to perceive the position and movement of their own body without relying on visual or auditory cues. This sense is made possible by specialized receptors located in muscles, tendons, and joints that send information to the brain about the body's position, tension, and movement. Proprioception plays a critical role in movement control, balance, and coordination and is essential for a wide range of activities, from simple tasks like walking and grasping objects to complex activities like playing sports and performing dance routines.

Fine motor skills and their operation fall under proprioception and the associated difficulties. Random arm and leg movements are a result of the brain's proprioceptive communication in children. Muscle control can also be challenging, meaning that children may exert too much force without realizing it. The following sensory supporting devices can be used:

- Creating an obstacle course at home.

- Throwing a tennis ball back and forth.

- Lifting and replacing heavy objects.

- Jumping on trampolines.

- Massages involving different levels of pressure.

Learning the words that are associated with the feelings and sensitivities will help you better understand your child or student and their struggles and emotions. The words we use to communicate with them can be harmful or helpful. Speak respectfully to your children. Your words can show that you value them and will eventually become the words they hear in their heads (self-talk). If we want to teach boundaries, expectations, and consequences, our goal is to do it by talking in such a way that they learn something but do not feel afraid, belittled, or stupid.

Consider the following options:

- Calm down, versus I see you are having a hard time.

- It's no big deal. It's just a fire truck versus if you need to cover your ears, that's okay.

- Big boys can sit through a haircut versus I understand it's hard for you. Let's take a break.

If we stop and think about how paramount it is to have

a regulated and balanced nervous system, we may realize how in vain some of the things we've been trying to teach our children have been. Teaching social skills and improving executive function are areas of difficulty for many children and adults with Autism and ADHD. Parents and educators often attempt to improve these skills as it is often blatantly apparent that they are areas of need. However, our ability to make gains in those areas may not be entirely possible if our level of arousal is not ideal. The emotions that go along with anxiety or anger can shut down one's awareness and ability to process what's going on around them. Those mirror neurons mentioned earlier in this chapter are visible in MRI studies. They are believed to be required to learn and apply social skills. Although they are visible, they have not turned on because the body isn't regulated. The lack of organizational skills that is a struggle for so many children is much more possible when the body isn't in a constant state of unbalanced arousal.

The Zones of Regulation

Leah Kuypers, the creator of the Zones of Regulation curriculum, is an OT who specializes in social learning and self-regulation. She is a graduate of both the University of Wisconsin-Madison and the University of St. Paul, with vast experience in her field. Kuypers' motivation for creating the curriculum came from her observations of the difficulties that her students had with regulation and emotional control (Kuypers, 2014). She describes the curriculum as follows:

A systematic, cognitive-behavioral approach is used to

teach us how to regulate our feelings, energy, and sensory needs in order to meet the demands of the situation around us and be successful socially.

There are four zones, which are determined by feelings and current state, into which autistic children fit, depending on outside factors. Each zone is comparable to traffic signs and their meanings.

The Red Zone (Stop Sign)

Heightened states of alertness and intense emotions fit into this zone. For instance, terror, anger, devastation, or elation.

The Yellow Zone (Proceed With Caution)

The yellow zone is also associated with heightened emotions that lean towards the intense side. However, this zone occupies more control over feelings such as excitement, frustration, anxiety, or nervousness.

The Green Zone (Good to Go)

A calmer state of alertness is categorized by the green zone, which provides the best learning conditions. Emotions, such as happiness, focus, and willingness to be taught, are found within the green zone.

The Blue Zone (Rest and Re-energize)

The blue zone is used to describe low levels of alertness, like sadness or boredom.

Transitions Between Zones

We must remember that there is nothing wrong or abnormal about the emotional experiences in each zone. Still, it can be challenging to transition from one zone to the other. That is where the learning comes in. It is important to teach children to identify what zone they are occupying and how to manage that zone, taking into consideration the environment and circumstances.

Think back to your school days and the transition between the excitement and erratic nature of the playground to the calm and structured environment in the classroom. The yellow zone excitement, provided by playground activities, needs to transition into the calm focus of the green zone to best promote learning. That transition becomes easier if a child can identify which zone they are in and when to move to another zone, as is the goal of Leah Kuypers' curriculum.

Benefits

The zones are inclusionary for all neurodivergent children. Positive social and emotional learning is most often the result of the curriculum, and the language used during implementation is neutral and simple. Teachers, and the children being taught, continue to benefit mutually from the curriculum, which is a testament to its success.

Parents may find it beneficial to use the poster or printout of the zones (or something similar) at home. You can have it laminated and then attach photos of the child (which can be moved around on the chart) according to how they feel at a particular moment. This can be super helpful in putting feelings into pictures and words. When we know exactly what's going on with our children, we are better equipped to help them deal with things. They may need help figuring out how to feel more alert or de-escalate. They may need a break before they transition from one activity to the next, or they may fare better if we reduce the demands on them.

Chapter 3

Eight Parts of Communication

Humans are unique among all other species in the world in that they are self-conscious. We have some of the most sophisticated and nuanced forms of communication. People of all ages and from all walks of life must be able to effectively communicate if they are to survive. The process by which individuals of any species or civilization exchange thoughts, knowledge, emotions, details, and points of view with one another can be referred to as communication. A conversation may have a variety of objectives. The most frequent purpose, however, is to enable people who belong to the same species or civilization to understand one another better.

This is no different when it comes to neurodivergent children as well. These children and adolescents communicate for the same reason as everybody else does. There are a variety of reasons why neurodivergent children can have an especially hard time trying to put their thoughts into words. How can we help give them the words?

To better understand the complexity of communication, let's look at the several processes that are involved in carrying out a conversation. The communication process can be divided into eight crucial parts, each of which performs a vital role in the process as a whole:

- source

- message

- channel

- receiver

- feedback

- environment

- context

- interference

Source

The message is conceived by the source, which also produces and transmits it. The information is either presented to or sent to the audience (receiver) after the source has encoded it by selecting the precise sequence of words or the most appropriate phrases to communicate the intended meaning. The source can determine how effectively the audience has understood the message by monitoring the audience's response and then providing clarification or additional information.

Message

The stimulus or meaning that is created by the source for the receiver or audience is what is referred to as the message. The message is not just about the meaning that is communicated through the use of words but also about how the meaning is communicated through nonverbal cues, structure, grammar, style, and other components.

Channel

The channel can be thought of as the path that a message or messages take from the sender to the recipient. Face-to-face interactions, speeches, phone calls, voicemails, radio, public address systems, and Zoom are all examples of spoken channels. Letters, memos, purchase orders, invoices, articles published in newspapers and magazines, blogs, emails, text messages, tweets, and other forms of written communication are examples of written channels. It's also important to note that neurodivergent individuals may use multiple communication methods to convey a message, including spoken language, written language, and nonverbal communication, such as sign language and AAC. And even if an individual uses one communication method, it does not mean that it is the only one they understand. Therefore, it's important to be open and to use multiple forms of communication in order to facilitate effective communication with a neurodivergent person.

Receiver

The receiver takes the message from the source and then analyzes and interprets the message in a variety of ways, some of which the originator may not have intended. As a result, sometimes messages are misinterpreted by the listener. Some neurodivergent individuals may have difficulty processing verbal language, which can make it hard for them to understand spoken or written messages. There are multiple reasons why that may occur. Here are a few examples:

Difficulty With Social Cues

Many neurodivergent individuals may have difficulty interpreting nonverbal cues, such as facial expressions, body language, and tone of voice. This can make it hard for them to understand the intended meaning of a message.

Difficulty With Abstract Concepts

Some neurodivergent individuals may have difficulty understanding abstract concepts, such as sarcasm, idioms, and figurative language.

Limited Perspective-Taking

Some neurodivergent individuals may have difficulty understanding the perspective of others, which can make it hard for them to understand the intended meaning of a message.

Difficulty With Memory

Some neurodivergent individuals may have difficulty remembering and processing information, which can make it hard for them to understand and retain new information.

Limited or Specific Interest

Some neurodivergent individuals may have a limited or specific interest that could cause them to interpret information or messages in a specific way that is related to their interests.

It's important to note that neurodivergent individuals may all have different difficulties and strengths. Therefore, it's vital to be patient and flexible and to use multiple forms of communication in order to facilitate effective communication with a neurodivergent person.

Difficulty Understanding and Using Verbal Language

Some neurodivergent individuals may have difficulty processing verbal language, which can make it hard for them to understand spoken or written messages.

Difficulty With Social Cues

Many neurodivergent individuals may have difficulty interpreting nonverbal cues, such as facial expressions, body language, and tone of voice. This can make it hard for them to understand the intended meaning of a message.

Difficulty With Abstract Concepts

Some neurodivergent individuals may have difficulty understanding abstract concepts, such as sarcasm, idioms, and figurative language.

Limited Perspective-Taking

Some neurodivergent individuals may have difficulty understanding the perspective of others, which can make it hard for them to understand the intended meaning of a message.

Difficulty With Memory

Some neurodivergent individuals may have difficulty remembering and processing information, which can make it hard for them to understand and retain new information.

Visual/Spatial

The visual learner creates an image in their head that corresponds to what they have just learned. They favor the dissemination of information over a solitary writing approach that simply uses words. Students who major in spatial studies typically have highly developed senses of smell and hearing but have trouble listening to others.

Because spatial learners are visual by nature, they are adept at reading both people and situations by taking in the details of their surroundings, including body language and facial expressions.

It's important to note that different neurodivergent individuals may have different difficulties and strengths. Therefore, it's important to be patient and flexible and to use multiple forms of communication in order to facilitate effective communication with a neurodivergent person.

Feedback

You are providing feedback whenever you respond to the source, whether your response is purposeful or unintentional. The messages that are sent from the receiver back to the source are what make-up feedback. Whether verbal or nonverbal, all of these feedback signals enable the source to determine how successfully and accurately the message was received, as well as how poorly and inaccurately it was received.

Environment

The atmosphere, both physically and psychologically, in which you transmit and receive messages is referred to as the environment. Your environment, the people in it, animals, and even technology can all have an impact on how you communicate.

Context

The context of the communication contact includes the individuals engaged, the scenario they are in, and the environment in which they find themselves. Business attire is one example of the environmental cues that could be present in a professional communication setting. These cues can have a direct or indirect impact on the participants' expectations for language and behavior.

Interference

Interference, often known as noise, can originate from a variety of different sources. "Interference" refers to anything that gets in the way of or alters the meaning of the message that was intended by its source. This may be something exterior, or it may be something internal or psychological. The usual processes of encoding and decoding the message that is transmitted via the channel between the source and the receiver are disrupted by noise.

Chapter 4

Language Learning Styles

Everyone has their unique qualities, and this is something that rings especially true when it comes to the acquisition of any new talent. Languages included.

You might be familiar with or have heard material about the various learning styles and how it is possible to become a more effective language student by adapting your study methods to fit your unique learning style.

The reality, though, is that there is a great deal more nuance involved than that.

Study after study in the realm of science has come to the same conclusion: there is no clear answer. That is to say: It is not at all obvious whether adapting one's tactics for learning a language (or any learning strategy) to the most effective learning style would result in improved retention of the information that has been learned.

If one doesn't try to figure out which learning style one likes and instead just utilizes tactics that are tailored to that style, one might be able to obtain outcomes that are on par with those that they would get if they learned using a method that wasn't their natural inclination.

Your motivation will remain high, and the experience will continue to be enjoyable if you tailor your learning to focus more on your preferred learning method. It is not enough to just complete activities that are a perfect match for your unique method of learning. It's best to use a variety of approaches to education.

All of this is increasingly important when it comes to neurodivergent children learning a language. At times, acquiring the correct words can be a challenge for neurotypicals. Tailoring a neurodivergent child's learning experience to their preferred learning style will make them keener to continue learning and, as a result, reap far better rewards.

Let's take a look at different learning styles and some examples of them:

Visual or Spatial Learners

A visual learning style refers to how individuals learn and process information through visual cues, such as images, diagrams, videos, and other types of visual aids. Some examples of visual learning strategies include:

• Using flashcards to memorize information.

• Creating charts or diagrams to organize information.

- Drawing or sketching to understand new concepts.

- Using images or videos to supplement reading or lectures.

Some of the benefits of visual learning include:

- Enhancing memory retention.

- Creating a deeper understanding of concepts.

- Making learning more interactive.

- Engaging in improving problem-solving skills.

Spatial learning style refers to how individuals learn and process information through spatial cues, such as shapes, patterns, and visual-spatial relationships. Some examples of spatial learning strategies include:

- Using maps and graphs to understand information.

- Using mental imagery to recall information.

- Building 3D models to understand concepts.

- Playing spatial reasoning games.

Likewise, the benefits of spatial learning include:

- Improving spatial reasoning skills.

- Enhancing problem-solving abilities.

- Creating a deeper understanding of concepts.

- Enhancing memory retention.

Visual language learners do very well when they supplement their lessons with charts and color-code concepts in order to make the knowledge easier to remember. People who remember information better when it is presented in a visual format, such as a table, picture, graph, or presentation, are the best candidates for this type of learning style.

Visual learners sometimes struggle in traditional classrooms because of the excessive amount of information presented in a sequential fashion, but verbal and analytical learners flourish in these settings.

Consider the construction of a miniature airplane, for instance. Some children are able to put the puzzle together just by looking at the individual parts, while others require step-by-step visual directions. They are unable to participate in any activity unless they have a complete understanding of the situation.

For the same reason, people do not always pay attention to the details. Concepts are only retained in the memories of spatial learners when they are connected to other concepts or visualized in their minds.

Engaging in activities such as the arts, building blocks, video games, photography, architecture, or engineering are excellent choices for students who learn best through the use of their visual and spatial abilities.

It's important to note that people may have a preference for one or multiple learning styles. Also, some individuals may not have a preference for any particular learning style. Furthermore, people tend to use different learning strategies depending on the task or subject matter. Therefore, it's important to be open to different forms of learning and not to limit oneself to a single learning style.

Aural or Auditory Learners

Aural learning style refers to the way in which individuals learn and process information through sound and music. Some examples of aural learning strategies include:

- Listening to music or audio recordings to memorize information.
- Using mnemonic devices such as rhymes or songs to remember information.
- Listening to lectures or presentations.

The benefits of aural learning include:

- Enhancing memory retention.

- Creating a deeper understanding of concepts.

- Making learning more interactive and engaging.

- Improving problem-solving skills.

Auditory learning style refers to the way in which individuals learn and process information through verbal or spoken language. Some examples of auditory learning strategies include:

- Listening to lectures or presentations.

- Participating in group discussions.

- Reading aloud or recording oneself while studying.

- Using verbal cues or mnemonics to remember information.

The pros of the auditory learning style can include:

- Improving listening and verbal communication skills.

- Enhancing problem-solving abilities.

- Enhancing memory retention.

Aurals favor being told how to do something verbally rather than reading the instructions. They are articulate, have good recall, and are great at telling stories, explaining their ideas, speaking in public, and remembering knowledge. Additionally, they are very good at remembering information. You are most likely an auditory learner if you find that you are able to solve difficulties by talking about them out loud, even to yourself, and if you enjoy participating in study groups.

These pupils may benefit from traditional education

because they have no problem following dictation and engaging in activities that need repetition. When it comes to acquiring a new language, students who learn best through aural means gain by practicing with a second person, recording their lessons, questioning their teachers, instructing others, and taking part in classroom debates.

Verbal or Linguistic Learners

Verbal learning style refers to how individuals learn and process information through the use of spoken or written language. Verbal learning strategies can include:

- Reading and writing to understand and retain information.

- Participating in group discussions and debates.

- Using verbal cues or mnemonics to remember information.

- Summarizing information in writing or verbally.

Verbal learning is particularly helpful in improving reading and writing skills, enhancing memory retention, and improving problem-solving skills.

Linguistic learning style refers to the way in which individuals learn and process information through the use of language and communication, such as verbal or written language. Still, it includes the study of language, grammar, vocabulary, and other linguistic elements. Linguistic learning strategies often include reading and writing to understand and retain information, studying grammar and vocabulary, participating in language learning classes, and analyzing literature.

Linguistic learning is beneficial for improving language skills, creating a deeper understanding of language and communication, and improving problem-solving skills.

Individuals who take pleasure in acquiring knowledge via the study of language in any of its forms can consider adopting the linguistic learning style. They are able to comprehend and recall an idea more easily when it is presented to them using wordplay, metaphors, analogies, and rhymes.

Words and expressions from their expanded vocabularies are easily retained by them and transformed into stuff that is immediately used in their thoughts. They are the ones who read the entire book even though their homework simply requires them to read the first chapter because they thrive on reading and writing exercises.

Verbal learners benefit tremendously by participating in role plays and group discussions. When a person is learning a second language, it is simple for them to recall words and idioms, link those words and idioms to other people, and finally express themselves using the new language.

Because they have an interest in literature, there is a good chance that they will begin reading for pleasure in their second language. This will both hasten their progress and make it easier for them to retain the material.

People who prefer to read books versus watching movies

have a certain type of learning style that correlates to their preference. They are good listeners and have a tendency to do well on tests. They also keep journals, love tongue twisters, and learn new words.

Social Learning Style

Social learning style is the way in which individuals learn and process information through social interactions and interactions with others. Some examples of social learning strategies are:

- Collaborating with peers to solve problems or complete projects.

- Participating in group discussions and debates.

- Learning through mentorship or apprenticeship.

- Observing and imitating the behavior of others.

These strategies are helpful in:

- Improving communication and teamwork skills.

- Enhancing problem-solving abilities.

- Creating a deeper understanding of society.

- Building confidence and self-esteem.

- Creating opportunities for feedback and constructive criticism.

• Developing a sense of belonging and connectedness.

People who enjoy and get the most out of social engagement are characterized by this type of learning style. They learn valuable information via group conversations, group lessons, and collaboration that they participate in.

Social learners can flourish with the help of role-playing and question-and-answer sessions. They can easily read people, including interpreting their body language, tone of voice, and emotions displayed on their faces. This ability is referred to as "people smart." They may have difficulty completing their assignments and projects on their own, but they are eager to participate in class, ask questions, and make new friends.

Those who are social learners and study languages will benefit from having homework that entails conducting interviews with other people, collaborating with others, or attending group sessions. They would benefit from meeting new people and sharing their knowledge with others because it is both significant and beneficial to them.

Physical Learners

Physical learning style is the way in which individuals learn and process information through physical movement and hands-on activities. Some examples of physical learning strategies include:

• Using manipulatives or hands-on materials to understand and retain information.

- Engaging in movement or physical activity while studying.

- Using visual aids or diagrams to understand concepts.

- Using mnemonic devices that involve physical movement.

Benefits of physical learning include:

- Enhancing muscle-memory.

- Improving problem-solving skills.

- Making learning more interactive and engaging.

- Improving motor skills.

- Helping people to engage with the material in a more meaningful way.

Physical language learners flourish from physical contact and manipulating materials. Learners who benefit most from tactile experiences are those who profit from learning by doing and through hands-on activities such as sketching, playing with clay, working puzzles, dancing, modeling, and role-playing.

Online language instruction is beneficial for students who have a style of learning that is similar to this one. They find that studying on rocking chairs, chewing gum, and clicking pens is helpful. They find that writing things down helps them recall them better, but they have difficulty following instructions. The thought of being forced to sit motionlessly for long periods of time and having to concentrate for extended periods of time can feel like a nightmare.

Students who learn better through kinesthetic activities like making posters, going on field trips, conducting experiments, and creating collages are more likely to create diagrams, charts, and concept maps than auditory learners are.

Natural Learners

Natural learning is a style of learning that emphasizes the use of real-life experiences and hands-on activities to acquire knowledge and skills. It is based on the idea that people learn best when they are actively engaged in experiences that are relevant to their interests and needs.

Examples of natural learning include:

- Gardening and farming as a way to learn about botany and ecology.

- Cooking as a way to learn about nutrition and chemistry.

- Building and repairing as a way to learn about physics and engineering

- Traveling as a way to learn about different cultures and geography.

Benefits of natural learning include:

- Increased engagement and motivation as the learning is relevant and interesting to the learner

- Development of practical skills that can be immediately applied in real-life situations.

- Greater retention of information as the learning is reinforced through hands-on experiences.

- Development of a deeper understanding of the subject matter as the learner is able to make connections between the material and their own experiences.

Activities that require hands-on participation can also be beneficial for students who learn in a natural way. Lessons taught outside are empowering for students who are driven by their senses and who have a passion for nature, discovery, and investigation.

Natural learners would thrive in non-traditional educational environments like those provided by Montessori and other similar institutions. They tend to have an interest in animals, geology, the environment, and weather. Natural learners have an advantage in these fields because of their close connection to the natural world. They are able to conduct research, investigate subjects, and keep a diary about their discoveries when they are learning languages. In addition, many have the ability to generate writings about topics associated with biology, environmental news, and non-fiction literature.

Analytic Learners

Logical learning, also called analytical learning, refers to the style of learning that emphasizes the use of reasoning and critical thinking to acquire knowledge and skills. It is based on the idea that people learn best when they are presented with logical explanations and can see the connections between different concepts and ideas.

Links With Savants

This may seem like a bit of a tangent, but due to the literal and logical tendency of many autistic individuals, math skills can often be excellent. The Merriam-Webster definition of a savant is as follows:

A person affected with a developmental disorder (such as autism or intellectual disability) who exhibits exceptional skill or brilliance in some limited field (such as mathematics or music).

It makes sense that many autistic individuals are good at math. Interestingly, music is similar to math in that there is a specific formula that never changes. Take guitar, for instance. If you push down on a certain string and then pluck it, the sound will always be the same. If you then put your finger in a different place and pluck the string, the sound will be different from the first sound, but with that finger position, the sound will never differ from itself. Essentially both math and guitar/music are logical.

Further examples of logical learning include analyzing

scientific experiments as a way to learn about cause-and-effect relationships. Debating is a way to learn about different perspectives and reasoning, which often doesn't come as easily as playing strategy games as a way to learn about problem-solving and logic.

Further benefits of logical learning include the development of critical thinking skills, which are valuable in many areas of life. Increased ability to understand and analyze complex information, greater understanding of the relationships between different concepts and ideas, and improved problem-solving skills, as the learner is able to break down and analyze problems logically. A stark benefit of this type of thinking and the application thereof is the adversity, probably sub-conscious to snap decisions. Contrast that with a bipolar individual in a manic phase, and decide what type of thinking would be more conducive to good decision-making. The answer is obvious.

The Framing Effect

We often see this in marketing and advertising. For example, you're looking for a dress, and you see two adverts:

- Blue dress for sale at $75

- Blue dress on sale at 50% off the usual price of $150

The illusion that most customers would succumb to is the perceived $75 saving, even though both offers have an identical purchase price. In the literal analytical and logical mind of an autistic individual, option 1 is the likely choice.

Analytical/Logical Learning

The analytical learning approach is excellent for quickly recognizing patterns and trends in any form of data. They never stop looking for the reasons or causes behind things, in addition to the consequences that can be shown objectively. The ability to interpret all of them, make logical inferences, and draw relationships is a strength of logical learners.

The learner who thinks analytically is fascinated by finding out how things function. Logic and structures fascinate them, and they take great pleasure in developing efficient, well-thought-out procedures for themselves and others.

They are masters in finding solutions to difficult problems and conundrums. You'll have no trouble recognizing them because they constantly question, "Why?" They have a natural tendency to reason and arrive at conclusions based on data. One of their major skills is their ability to memorize equations and information.

People who prefer material to be delivered sequentially and who prefer to tackle one challenge at a time are associated with this type of learning style. They are really attentive to the smallest of details.

Logical students do well in traditional educational settings because those environments encourage them to take notes, do self-evaluations, and learn from their own mistakes. When taking part in a group activity or when confronted with anything that they believe defies logic, it drives them to frustration. They thrive when there is both structure and routine in their lives.

When students are learning a new language, they want to have scheduled courses and a clear curriculum so that they can track their progress and make the most of the time they spend studying.

Group Learners Versus Individual Learners

Group learners are individuals who prefer to learn in a group setting, where they can interact with their peers and receive feedback and support from others. This type of learning environment allows them to collaborate and share ideas, and they often feel more motivated and engaged when learning in a group.

Examples of group learning include study groups for a class or exam, team projects, discussions or debates, and collaborative problem-solving activities.

Individual learners, on the other hand, prefer to learn independently and at their own pace. They often prefer to work alone and can become easily distracted in group settings. They tend to be self-motivated and self-disciplined, and they often prefer to learn through reading, writing, and solitary problem-solving.

Examples of individual learning are self-study and independent research, solo projects or assignments, reading, and taking notes alone to reflect on later.

Students that have this type of learning style are most successful when they carry out activities such as research, homework, or exercises independently. They believe that when they work on a problem on their own, they are able to solve it more quickly and effectively.

Individualized instruction is beneficial for individuals learning a second language on their own, regardless of whether the instruction is delivered in-person, virtually, or through a combination of the two. One-on-one time with professors allows students to make more concentrated efforts in their advancement and increases the likelihood that they will be recognized for their unique achievements.

Learners that pursue their education on their own are self-driven, focused, and driven to succeed. Only when they are engaged in their academic pursuits are they likely to be solitary.

In contrast, some students learn best when they are among others. Being part of a group can sometimes motivate students to push themselves or try harder because they are thinking about what others in the group think about them. Other benefits of group learning are that it enhances communication and other professional development skills.

It's important to note that most people have a combination of both learning preferences, it's not only about being one type of learner but also, depending on the task and the subject, one may prefer a different learning style.

Chapter 5

Types of Language Processing

Children can develop language in different ways, two of which are as follows:

1. Analytical

2. Gestalt

Analytical Language Learners

Most neurotypicals analytically develop language. These children pay attention to and pick up on the meaning of individual words. After that, they may use that word in other circumstances before eventually fusing it with other words to create phrases and sentences. For example, a child may say milk when they see or want milk. They learn that the word for milk is used whether it comes from a jug, carton, cup, bottle, or from their mother's breast. They may begin to pair the word milk with another word after they have approximately fifty words in their repertoire.

For example, they may say "more milk" or "want milk." As they age and are exposed to more language, the average length of children's utterances will become longer. By age five or six, we would expect a sentence such as, "Mom, can I have milk, please?" Intonation use and understanding develop as a child gets older. Analytic language processors focus heavily on grammar from two to three years of age. As a result, their language is both flexible and productive. Most neurotypical children learn language this way.

Gestalt Language Learners

Gestalt language learners acquire language differently. They begin learning language by memorizing entire phrases rather than learning the meaning of one word at a time. The meaning of the words that make up those statements is then learned backward. Although some echolalia occurs naturally as a component of ordinary language development, many children often utilize both delayed and immediate echolalia. Echolalia used to be regarded as having no real meaning. Thus, statements like "You want some more?" were seen as the child repeating what they had heard before. But the recent researchers who promote neurodiversity are beginning to realize that is only sometimes the case.

Echolalia is sometimes referred to as scripting. Echolalia can look like the repetition of sounds, phrases, and movies from TV shows, humming, whistling, or singing. Other forms of echolalia may look like: copying any noise like a car or animal, as well as repeating words and phrases, including the tone in which it is produced. Echolalia can be defined as the literal and rote repetition of the speech of others. Echolalia presents as either immediate or delayed. Words repeated immediately or after a short time are referred to as immediate echolalia. This repetition can look like a single-word repetition at the end of a sentence, for example:

Adult: Are you hungry?

Child: Hungry.

It can also be a complete phrase repetition:

Adult: Let's get your shoes.

Child: Let's get your shoes.

Words that are heard by the child and are stored in their minds and then repeated after a long interval are referred to as delayed echolalia. Delayed echolalia can occur for a variety of reasons. Let's look at an example. A child may say: "line up at the door." He may be saying this phrase in his home because he wants to go somewhere, or he could be saying it because he is thinking about school, or he overheard you talking to someone about his teacher, and that phrase is something the teacher says every day.

Another example would be a family driving in a car, and as a particular song plays on the radio, it starts to rain. You, as the parent, say, "Oh no, would ya look at this."

Two weeks later, the family is having a sunny Saturday afternoon barbeque while music plays in the background. The same song that was playing in the car sounds out of the radio at the barbecue, and your daughter says, "Oh no, would ya look at this." You can't work out why your daughter said those words. Now, every time she hears that song, she says, "Oh no! Would ya look at this!"... and you, as a parent, are confused as heck. The reason, however, is that she associated the statement with the song instead of the weather.

If the echolalia is an exact repetition, it is known as "pure." On the other hand, "mitigated" echolalia occurs when the child changes the original speaker's wording or intonation. As the child's understanding of language improves, an increase in mitigated echolalia may be observed.

Some children get great joy out of scripting familiar sounds or lines from their favorite people, movies, or songs. Some children use it to reassure themselves or to calm and cope with a stressful moment.

What Should You Do as a Parent if Your Child Communicates Via Echolalia?

There is nothing inherently wrong about being echolalic. As parents, we want our children to learn and grow and communicate with others. It is how we can share information and get our needs met. So, when toddlers or school-age children communicate with others, we want them to express themselves in a way that feels right and meets their needs. So, if the function of the echolalia is just to say something aloud because it has entertainment value, the speaker, if capable, might want to communicate that to the listener by saying something like, "I keep thinking about the movie Star Wars." It is especially crucial to convey this when the word, phrase, or sentence is off-topic or otherwise random to clarify why the phrase was said.

Remember that phrases spoken, or songs sung by a Gestalt Language Processor can have several different purposes. So, when a child is singing "itsy bitsy spider," they may think about a cute little spider climbing up a waterspout, or they may say it because they want to play with you. If and when we are not sure of the purpose of the echolalia, we must acknowledge that it is still communication and that we are listening but try to assign meaning to the utterance only if it is reasonably obvious.

Another example of delayed echolalia:

You are in the car line picking your child up from school. He gets into the car, and after you greet him, he says, "Are you thirsty"? What's happening here may need to be clarified initially because you think he is asking you a question. You may answer him by saying, "No, I'm not thirsty," only to realize he is asking you repeatedly. Your child memorized that statement as a whole, even though they might not have understood the meaning of each word. You then realize he doesn't want to know if you are thirsty; he has learned that when he hears that phrase, someone hands him a cup with a drink. He meant to communicate that he was thirsty. So, we now have to figure out how to give him the right words! The next time, before handing him the drink, you take his hand and gesture as if he is tapping his chest, and you model the words you want him to use, "I'm thirsty," and then hand him the drink. You have, then, just given him the words! Speaking from the child's frame of reference versus our own will help children who are echolalic know what to say. I always try to make sure I am making things as clear as possible for the child by making my comments or questions have a more dramatic tone, as well as prompting them somehow to indicate that we are referring to them.

If the child finds enjoyment through scripting favorite lines from movies at a time when you want their attention to be elsewhere, you can say something like, "I hear that you are thinking about the Toy Story movie. We are discussing what we will do after dinner tonight, so let's discuss that." By doing this, we are not abandoning the idea that the script may have some other meaning, as in the previous example about the doctor's office. Instead, we are trying to keep the topic of conversation clear.

Suppose the child is using scripting because they are anxious and need to self-regulate, calm, and provide self-reassurance; we would want to work toward finding additional calming and coping tools. Occupational therapy can be a wonderful resource. For example, the child may say, "Time to put your shoes on; it's OK," while having a major meltdown because they don't like how the shoes feel. We will not put them on the bus with bare feet, but we should still acknowledge their feelings about not wanting to wear the shoes. "I know you don't want to put your shoes on now, but it's time to go to school, and your feet are safe inside these shoes for now. I think we should look for a more comfortable pair this weekend, though."

It's essential to give him the most appropriate words from his frame of reference. For example, he is saying he doesn't want to wear the shoes, so we might want to model something like, "No shoes, please." When first learning the words, we want to honor the child's comments or requests, so they can connect what they say and the fact that it happens. For example, we would model or teach this when shoes are optional and then honor his request by allowing him to remain free of the shoes.

Rather than ask questions, it is better to model terms such as "Let's," "It's," and "I'm," so they are more likely to be communicating clearly. Intonation (the feeling behind the words) is another important tool that you can use to teach the words. So, when transitioning from the child's old phrase, "Are you thirsty?" to the phrase that reflects what they actually mean, "I'm thirsty," saying it with a strong emphasis on the "I'm" will make it more likely that the child will be able to remember and use it at the correct time. Keeping a record of your child's utterances can also be a helpful tool if you are willing to explore a little to figure out the meaning of the script based on how they are feeling at the moment. So, if your son says "Chika Chika Boom Boom" every time he is feeling ill, it may be because you read him that book the last time you were in the waiting room of the doctor's office. This scenario is an excellent example that echolalia is purposeful. He is communicating! We need to give him the words. "Let's go to the doctor" or "I'm sick" Delayed echolalia is often tied to things that are rich in emotions, so if you can pair the scripted phrase with a feeling or circumstance, you are more likely to discover the meaning of that phrase.

Hyperlexia

The term "hyperlexia" was first used in 1967. This characteristic is common in autism. Hyperlexic children are usually Gestalt Language Processors.

How we learn is influenced by how our brains process information. Children with autism frequently recognize the words but have trouble understanding the meaning of a sentence or paragraph. According to psychologist Robert Naseef, "This characteristic is common in autism. Children with autism often recognize the words but struggle to comprehend the meaning of the text or the paragraph" (Gordon, 2020). If a child can "read" before they are officially taught to read, they are likely hyperlexic. Once more, despite their ability to decipher the written language, young kids have trouble understanding what the paragraph is saying. So, they will see "ball" and be able to say "ball." When you or I see the word, and we say it (either in our heads or aloud), we are also picturing a ball in our minds. Hyperlexic children may or may not have that vision of the ball. Another example, they will see the words "Now it's time to go to the library," and they will say, "Now it's time to go to the library." These words do not necessarily conjure up thoughts of going to the library for the child. This difference between what they read and what they think is the comprehension piece that is often missing. So, when we think the child is reading, upon further evaluation, we realize they are indeed reading but not understanding. They also may need to learn the names of the individual letters or that words are symbols that represent real things. They may not know that we can combine letters to make words, combine words to make sentences, and combine sentences to make paragraphs. It's important to establish here that hyperlexia is not just an interest or obsession with lining up the letters of the alphabet in order from A to Z.

Regarding grammar, school-aged Gestalt language processors will not quickly understand how to put words together to say or write in more flexible ways.

We need to focus on the learning strengths of hyperlexic children and take into account the ways in which they are more likely to learn faster. Lists or instructions should be in bullet point form, with images next to the text. Explaining the "w" questions, such as "why," and then linking it to the start of the response "because" is a method that has proven effective. Interactive games and using a child's favorite points of interest, in addition to visual timetables, are also recommended.

Sign Language

While spoken language is certainly the more common means of communication, let's not forget about other forms of communication, such as sign language. I mentioned speech therapy in the echolalia section above, but it also applies to children that are completely non-verbal or that have difficulties speaking.

Adults and children are capable of expressing themselves

visually through hand gestures, body language, facial expressions, and sign language.

Although sign language is the primary means of communication for the Deaf and Hard-of-Hearing community, it can also be helpful to other social groups. Sign language may be useful for communication for those with difficulties, including Autism, Apraxia of speech, Cerebral Palsy, and Down syndrome.

There is no universally recognized sign language. There are many variations of sign languages because, like spoken languages, they evolved naturally via interaction between various groups of people. Between 138 and 300 different sign languages are currently in use all over the world.

It's interesting to note that most nations with similar spoken languages do not necessarily have the same sign language. American Sign Language (ASL), British Sign Language (BSL), and Australian Sign Language are three variants of English, for instance (Auslan).

Recent years have seen an uptick in the popularity of introducing sign language to infants and toddlers. Some parents may be concerned that teaching their child sign language would impede their child's verbal development.

Research indicates that this is not the case. In fact, often, the use of signs paired with spoken words can lead to an increase in verbal abilities.

It's vital to differentiate between speech and language as a first step. Words are uttered using a sound process known as speech. It's the science of making sounds by manipulating the muscles in your mouth and airflow. The ability to communicate with others is facilitated by the use of language. Any combination of spoken words, physical actions, and graphic signs is possible.

Studies have revealed that exposing infants to sign language has no negative effects on their language development. The use of sign language has been shown to promote and stimulate linguistic growth. Simply put, it helps children get started with language sooner. Also, there are many benefits to learning a second language, both for verbal and nonverbal communication.

The five main benefits are:

1. Increased vocabulary.

2. Reduced temper tantrums due to boredom or dissatisfaction.

3. Growing capacity for social interaction.

4. Increased comprehension.

5. Increased production of more advanced linguistic skills

Early exposure to sign language has benefited a wide range of populations. Inclusion of children with expressive language difficulties, such as those caused by speech delays, Down syndrome, autism, and apraxia. Providing a method of communicating via sign is an additional way of communicating with your child with or without using spoken words.

In a nutshell, learning sign language can help a child's verbal and linguistic growth. Negative social behaviors are mitigated, positive ones are fostered, and mental frameworks are developed. When introduced at an early age, sign language aids in a child's emotional, social, and academic growth as well as linguistic development.

The use of a few simple hand signs not only assist newborns in communicating but also improve their parents' capacity to comprehend what it is that their babies are attempting to convey. Dialing down the frustration of not being able to communicate can help crank up their confidence that you will listen and respond.

Speech sounds develop during the early childhood years. Should there be no other mitigating factors, such as a difference in the oral cavity or dentition, we expect the latest developing speech sounds to develop between ages 5 and 8.

Is your toddler saying "dog"? Or is it "Dad"? And how can you distinguish whether they are attempting to tell you that they want more mashed sweet potatoes or that they want to get down from their high chair? It might be challenging to make sense of your baby's earliest attempts at communication, including their first words. This is especially true when the word is not accompanied by the item the child is referring to or if they are not using gestures.

Again, self-assurance is another benefit that can accrue to parents who study sign language, particularly first-time mothers and fathers. Learning baby signals cannot only help you and your baby communicate more effectively with one another, but it will also aid in the development of your baby's motor abilities. It may even increase their intelligence.

What Does Baby Sign Language Exactly Entail?

Baby sign language is frequently derived from American Sign Language (ASL), while some instructors may teach a variant of this language. The focus is on keywords that are important in your baby's world (think of "milk," "up," and "done") and is extremely fundamental. There is no introduction to advanced grammar or other body language complexities associated with full nonverbal communication.

When Should I Start Teaching My Neurodivergent Child Sign Language?

Beginning your child's sign language education between the ages of six and eight months is an excellent time to do it. Researchers, however, suggest that parents evaluate not just their baby's readiness but also their own, as signing needs learning on the part of the parent as well as a commitment to a significant amount of repetition of the relevant hand signs. Some parents are ready to start when their newborns are just a few months old, but others wait until their tiny ones are closer to a year old.

Which Signs Should I Begin With?

There are a few very helpful words, although any term that pertains to your baby's world has the potential to be helpful. Functional signs are an excellent place to begin. Examples of such indications are "milk" and "eat." but the fun ones are actually important as well because these are what your child will probably be most interested in practicing with you, and that is why the fun ones are actually important as well. These may include signs such as "dog" if your canine companion is already your infant's closest companion or "bath" if your child adores spending time in the bathtub.

Introduce between one to three signals at a time, being sure to reiterate them frequently as though you were making solid claims and signing the phrases while saying them out loud simultaneously. Researchers recommend avoiding using the signals as inquiries because doing so can cause your child to get confused. In other words, you are signing "milk" as a statement, not signing "milk" to ask if he wants it.

The top eight signs that are beneficial for neurodivergent babies to learn:

- milk

- more

- all done

- pick me up (done as a single sign)

- help

- mom/dad

- give me

- eat

Augmentative and Alternative Communication

With all the information sharing on social media, the understanding and use of augmentative and alternative forms of communication are on the rise. The term "augmentative and alternative communication" refers to any technology, systems, tactics, or tools for communication that either completely replaces or supplements natural speech (AAC). A person who has difficulty communicating through speech may benefit from the use of these technologies.

The first "A" in AAC stands for Augmentative Communication. When something is augmented, it is added to or supplemented in some way. The addition of anything to one's speech or lack of speech is an example of augmentative communication (e.g., sign language, pictures, a letter board). Your message might become more understandable to your audience as a result of this. If a child's speech is moderate to severely unintelligible, they may benefit from the use of AAC.

The term "alternative communication" is represented

by the 2nd "A" in AAC. There can be several reasons why someone is or has become non-speaking; it may be temporary or permanent. Either way, an alternative way of communicating should be considered.

AAC can refer to tools, systems, equipment, or even methods in its most basic form. When a person is unable to rely on speech alone to communicate, these tools enable them to do so. It's possible that your child hasn't started talking yet. It's possible that you've lost your ability to communicate verbally. It's possible that your speech is inconsistent. If speaking is a challenging form of communication, AAC might be beneficial.

Who Does the AAC Serve?

There are a variety of circumstances that can prevent a person from effectively communicating through the use of voice. It's possible that they have a developmental issue that prevents them from developing speech properly. It's possible that a person had a brain injury that affects their ability to communicate verbally. AAC can be useful for a large number of people who struggle with a variety of communication issues, speech disorders, and speech impairments. Neurodivergent individuals benefit very much from AAC as well.

There are several different types of AAC, each with its own unique features and advantages.

Manual Communication Boards

These are communication boards that are held by the individual or their communication partner. They typically include a set of pictures or words that the individual can point to or use to express themselves.

Voice Output Devices

These devices speak for the individual, either through pre-recorded messages or by synthesizing speech. These devices can be portable and can vary from simple single message devices to more complex devices with multiple messages and capabilities like internet access.

Electronic Communication Devices

These devices are similar to Voice Output Devices. Still, they are more advanced and include a variety of features such as text-to-speech, email, and internet access.

Sign Language

Sign language is a visual form of communication that uses hand gestures, facial expressions, and body language to convey meaning. It is often used by individuals who are deaf or hard of hearing.

Speech Generating Devices

These devices enable the individual to produce speech by pressing a button or touching a screen. These devices can also include a variety of features, such as text-to-speech, email, and internet access.

Eye-gaze Systems

These systems allow individuals to communicate by using eye movements to select letters, words, or phrases from a computer screen.

It's imperative to understand that the most appropriate type of AAC will depend on the individual's specific needs and abilities. A speech-language pathologist or other professional can help determine the best AAC option for an individual.

Also, talk about how to find out what AAC is appropriate for your child's needs. Having a conversation without using words. It is challenging to communicate without using words. People who are unable to talk will be at a disadvantage in a world that is predominantly spoken. When messages cannot be conveyed clearly, it can be difficult and frustrating for everyone involved. This is frustrating for both the individual who is not speaking and the one with whom they are communicating.

People who are non-speakers frequently have a lot of thoughts that they want to convey to others. How do they communicate these ideas to others?

When a person is unable to communicate verbally, those around them frequently form opinions about their level of expertise, potential, and capacity to think and learn.

A person who is mute will quickly realize that there are certain things that are straightforward to communicate (e.g., reaching for the TV remote to suggest you want to change the channel). They also come to realize that there are some concepts that are difficult to convey (e.g., that the TV show reminds you of a family member who is gone).

What Different Kinds of AAC Are Utilized Most Frequently?

When a person is unable to speak, alternative and augmentative communication (AAC) refers to all of the tools and tactics that can be used to communicate with that person. Quite frequently,

we separate them into two categories: aided and unaided AAC.

Unaided AAC (Augmentative and Alternative Communication) refers to communication methods that do not require external aids or devices. Examples of unaided AAC include sign language, facial expressions, and gestures, which rely solely on the person's body and language skills.

Assisted AAC (Augmentative and Alternative Communication) refers to communication methods that require external aids or devices to supplement or replace speech. Examples of assisted AAC can include communication boards, choice cards, and photo exchange systems, which can support individuals with communication impairments to express their needs, thoughts, and ideas.

• symbol boards

- cards with a choice

- books about methods of communication

- PODD books

- keyboards with a chart of the alphabet

- gadgets that generate speech or devices that facilitate communication

- AAC apps on mobile devices

For communication support, we might employ a high-tech gadget like a voice-generating device or an app on a tablet or phone. As an alternative, we could use a manual or low-tech tool. a journal or book for communication.

An example of a high-tech augmentative and alternative communication device is Proloquo on the iPad (Printed Proloquo board)

AAC That Is Text-based

An augmentative and alternative communication (AAC) system may be a text-based system with a keyboard. This is typically for a person who composes their thoughts on the computer before speaking. They typically have reading and spelling abilities. AssistiveWare's alternative augmentative communication (AAC) solution is called Proloquo4Text.

AAC Based on Symbols

When it comes to communication, a lot of people need drawings or symbols. This includes those individuals who are unable to read or spell at this time. Words or even phrases could be represented by graphical symbols that we could introduce. They can easily read people, including interpreting their body language, tone of voice, and emotions displayed on their faces.

If you want to access some more information on AAC, there is a non-profit organization that focuses on education called MCIE. They are not specifically autism education structured, but there is a very interesting article on their blog, accompanied by videos made either by non-speaking autistic individuals or videos about AAC. Follow the link below:

www.thinkinclusive.us/post/videos-films-augmentative-alternative-communication

Chapter 6

Words at School

The Individuals with Disabilities Education Act (IDEA) is a federal law that mandates special education services to children with disabilities. The law has two primary components: Part B and Part C. Part B mandates special education services for children aged three to twenty-one. At the same time, Part C provides early intervention services to infants and toddlers aged zero to three.

Part C: Early Intervention Services

Part C of IDEA is designed to provide early intervention services to infants and toddlers with developmental delays or disabilities. Early intervention services are provided to children and their families from birth through age two. These services are designed to identify, evaluate, and provide early intervention services to children with disabilities to support their development and ensure they are ready for school when the time comes.

An Individualized Family Service Plan (IFSP) is a document developed for children with disabilities who are receiving early intervention services under Part C of IDEA.

The IFSP outlines the child's strengths and needs, as well as the goals and objectives of the early intervention services. It also includes information about the family's priorities, resources, and child development concerns.

To obtain an IFSP, parents must first request an evaluation from their local early intervention agency or state lead agency. The evaluation must be conducted within 45 days of the request. Once the evaluation is complete, the early intervention team, including the family, will meet to develop the IFSP. The team will include professionals from various disciplines, such as early childhood educators, therapists, medical professionals, and the child's family. The team will review assessment results, identify the child's strengths and needs, and develop measurable goals and objectives. The IFSP must be reviewed every six months and updated annually to ensure that the child's progress is monitored and that the services provided are appropriate for their needs.

Child Find: Part B

Child Find is a component of Part B of IDEA, which requires schools to identify and evaluate children with disabilities. The goal of Child Find is to locate and evaluate all children with disabilities, regardless of the severity of their condition. Child Find applies to children ages three to twenty-one, including children in private schools or the homeless.

Qualifying Conditions for IEP

To qualify for an Individualized Education Plan (IEP), a child must have one or more of the thirteen qualifying conditions listed under IDEA. These conditions include Autism, Deaf-Blindness, Deafness, Emotional Disturbance, Hearing Impairment, Intellectual Disability, Multiple Disabilities, Orthopedic Impairment, Other Health Impairments, Specific Learning Disability, Speech or Language Impairment, Traumatic Brain Injury, and Visual Impairment.

Getting an Evaluation: Starting the Process

Parents who suspect that their child may have a disability that requires special education services can initiate the evaluation process by contacting their child's school or local education agency (LEA). Once a request is made for an evaluation, the school must respond promptly and provide the parent with a copy of the procedural safeguards notice, which explains the parents' rights under IDEA.

Goals of Part C and Part B

The primary goal of Part C is to provide early intervention services to infants and toddlers with disabilities to support their development and ensure that they are ready for school when the time comes. The primary goal of Part B is to provide children with disabilities with free and appropriate public education (FAPE) in the least restrictive environment (LRE) possible. The LRE means that children with disabilities should be educated with their peers without disabilities to the maximum extent appropriate.

Procedural Safeguards

IDEA provides parents with procedural safeguards to ensure that they are involved in the decision-making process and that their child's rights are protected. Some of the procedural safeguards provided by IDEA include the right to obtain an independent evaluation, the right to participate in the development of their child's IEP, the right to access their child's educational records and the right to due process.

Federal vs. State Law Concerning IDEA

Under IDEA, each state is required to develop policies and procedures for providing special education services to children with disabilities. States must comply with the requirements of IDEA, but they also have the flexibility to implement their policies and procedures. State laws cannot conflict with IDEA but can provide additional protections and services for children with disabilities.

Although each state is required to comply with the requirements of IDEA, there may be some differences in how the law is implemented from state to state. Here are three examples of how the laws of IDEA may differ from state to state:

1. Eligibility Criteria: While the thirteen qualifying

conditions for receiving an IEP are set by federal law, states may have additional criteria for eligibility. For example, some states may require that a child's disability must have an adverse effect on their academic performance before they are eligible for an IEP, while other states may not have this requirement.

2. Timelines: IDEA sets specific timelines for various aspects of the special education process, such as the timeline for completing an evaluation or developing an IEP. However, states may have specific timelines that differ from federal timelines. For example, some states may require that an IEP meeting be held within a shorter timeframe than the federal requirement.

3. Procedural Safeguards: IDEA provides parents with procedural safeguards to protect their rights and ensure they are involved in decision-making. While federal law outlines these safeguards, states may have their own additional procedural safeguards. For example, some states may require that parents be provided with an interpreter or translator during the special education process if they do not speak English.

Chapter 7

Words at Home

Everyone should make an effort to gain an understanding of the notion of neurodiversity and incorporate it into their perspective of the world. Throughout human history, society has traditionally put the responsibility for socialization, communication, and "typical" behavior on individuals who are autistic or neurodiverse.

The concept of neurodiversity enables us to comprehend the many modes of relating to other people, talking with them, and existing in the world as merely the natural and typical variations that are inherent to the human experience. When we follow the tenets of neurodiversity, we cease trying to transform autistic and neurodivergent people to become more "normal" (or neurotypical). Instead, we seek to establish understanding across all different sorts of neurotypes. When viewed through this lens, validating and accepting individual ways of becoming the responsibility of each and every person.

There is no other setting that has a greater influence on

the experiences that a child has while growing up than their own home. Therefore, during the course of this chapter, we are going to talk about neurodiversity at home and what will help make your house more accepting of neurodiversity.

What can we do to make our homes more comfortable for neurodivergent children and adolescents? Here are a couple of things:

Provide a Secure Environment in Which Your Child Can Feel Comfortable Being Themselves

It is important for children to have the sense that they can be themselves when they are at home. There is a lot of demand in the outside world to comply with various forms of communication, thinking, and being. This pressure can make it difficult to be oneself. For neurodivergent adolescents, this can lead to masking or taking on behaviors that aren't true to who they are for the advantage of making others happy or comfortable.

In order to include activities that are accepting of neurodiversity in your household, encourage your children to investigate the various aspects of themselves that they might normally feel pressured to keep hidden from the rest of the world. Validate that it is okay for your autistic or neurodiverse child to stim freely in the comfort of their own home.

Become Aware of Your Child's Requirements and

Meet Them

Needs extend well beyond those that are often addressed in a class context as the fundamental requirements for surviving. Our requirements may be broken down into three categories: our physiological needs, which include things like the requirement for food, water, and shelter; our sensory needs; and our activity and interest needs. There is a good chance that your sensory needs, as well as the needs for activity and interest, will not be the same as those of your child.

Everyone, regardless of their neurotype, has a unique experience of the stimulus that their senses provide. This can include elements like lights, sounds, or even how clothing feels on the body. Getting to know what feels comfortable for your child's senses will allow you to change the environment to match their requirements.

Individuals have varying requirements in terms of their ideal activities and interests. A good life balance for many neurotypical people requires spending a significant amount of time in the company of other people. Alternately, the activity and interest needs of certain neurotypical individuals, as well as many neurodivergent individuals, revolve primarily around more solo pursuits.

Recognize That the Needs of Your Child May Differ From the Expectations that You Have of Them

If your child's neurotype is different from yours, it is essential to acknowledge the possibility that their requirements and your expectations will not align perfectly. The majority of individuals are made aware of the concept that there is a "typical" set of needs and that the things that many other people describe as needs are actually desires rather than necessities. It is essential to dispute this notion inside yourself (for example, why wouldn't we consider the needs of all people as valid?) and to make your child aware of the fact that various people have varied requirements in their lives.

If your child is neurotypical, this may look like helping them recognize that no, they do not get to have a fidget toy in class even though their neurodivergent peer does because their neurodivergent peer requires that fidget toy to be able to listen to the teacher's lesson, while they do not.

If you have a child who is neurodivergent, this may involve assisting them in understanding that it is acceptable to require the use of a fidget toy while in school, even while their peers do not. That is a need that they have, and it is important to remember that all needs are legitimate.

Let Your Child Communicate in the Methods That Are Most Comfortable for Them

Certain modes of communication, without a shadow of a doubt, receive the highest marks from society. The term "types" refers to both the mode of communication (such as expressive voice, gesture, American Sign Language, Alternative, and Augmentative Communication, etc.) as well as the style of communication (e.g., direct, indirect, tangential, etc.).

A child's unique form of communication and manner of expression can be validated in a straightforward manner by recognizing that the mode of expression they employ is not only entirely appropriate and valid but also does not require any sort of correction.

How many times have you encouraged your child to "use their words" if they speak a language that was traditionally spoken in your home? Why? Why is it necessary for your child to use words to communicate if they can show you what they want by reaching for something or pushing something away while it's in front of them? Their way of communicating is efficient and unambiguous!

Your ability to help your child in a way that affirms their neurodiversity will be enhanced if you allow your child the freedom to communicate in the ways that are most comfortable, natural, and efficient for them.

Foster Better Communication and Mutual Understanding Among Family Members

The first step in developing a home environment that is accepting of neurodiversity is being familiar with both yourself and your child. When you are able to notice the parallels as well as the differences in the needs and ways of being among the members of your family, you will be in a better position to address those differences with openness and curiosity.

Acceptance comes as a gift to us when we finally let go of the idea that neurotypical people are in the right and those with neurodivergent traits are in the wrong. We will stop fighting to change our children from who they are and instead focus on learning to understand them and assisting them in understanding that there are other ways of talking, socializing, and living that are equal.

Being a sibling of an autistic child is not the same as being a parent, and it has its own unique challenges. I am going to include a link to a video on an Australian parenting website, where siblings of children on the spectrum talk about their experiences and relationships. It features an 18-year-old university student called Eryl, who has a sister named Ellis, with Aspergers, and a 10-year-old called Bryce, who has two autistic siblings. It is very interesting and definitely worth a watch.

raisingchildren.net.au/autism/children-autism-videos/siblings-of-autistic-children

Challenges That Parents of Neurodivergent Children May Face

"Autism is part of my child, it's not everything he is. My child is so much more than a diagnosis" (Coehlo, n.d.).

Many parents who have children with autism are true superheroes. They provide a foundation of support and open doors for people who are exceptionally talented and have unique qualities. Every day presents the family with fresh obstacles to overcome as well as new chances. I have compiled a list of some of the most common difficulties that parents of children with ASD face on a daily or weekly basis in this part of the book.

The following is a list of common challenges that come with parenting a neurodivergent child:

Finances

When it comes to the cost of raising a child on the autism spectrum, some parents may feel overwhelmed by the long-term financial commitment. This might be the situation in households that do not have access to medical insurance, for example. The financial burden can manifest itself in a variety of ways, including the use of one's own vehicle rather than public transportation, the hiring of a carer on a regular basis, the giving up of a job in order to take care of the child, and the rising costs that are associated with the raising of a child. Having said that, we all have financial burdens to bear, and if we are smart as parents of autistic children, we can give our children what they need to function optimally without breaking the bank. Don't forget, as per the section on education in the previous chapter, the Individuals with Disabilities Education Act (IDEA) facilitates free public education to eligible children with disabilities throughout the United States. Some good planning and knowledge can save you money in a way that does not prejudice your child.

Stress and Lack of Time for Self-Care

It is not an easy undertaking to provide care for children who are autistic. It is not without its share of difficulties, strain, and ups and downs along the way. Because every child is different, providing care for children who have autism spectrum disorder (ASD) or any other neurodivergent disorder could be a full-time job for some families and parents. Every child has their own unique set of challenges, varying degrees of severity, and so on. Taking care of children is a source of stress for all types of families, particularly for single parents and nuclear families. Their already high levels of stress are made much worse by the fact that they may not have the support and aid of other family members or extended family members, etc.

When a parent or both parents do not have the assistance of a paid carer, extended family, or even close family members, they may find it difficult to provide enough care for their child, maintain good performance at one or more jobs, take care of the household, and multitask well. Because of this, they have very little time, if any, to spend on themselves. This could entail little to no opportunity for social interaction, rest, physical activity, the pursuit of hobbies and interests, and so on. The care of the child or adolescent with all of their particular intricacies can take precedence over the person's own identity, which could be pushed into the background. There are ways to take little breaks from life, so to speak, during which time you can display kindness towards yourself. Everyone will tell you that exercise is a great form of escapism. Think about it, if you're cranking the treadmill up to full speed, you definitely do not have the ability to stress and overthink. The additional positive element is dopamine production from physical activity. Maybe you enjoy swimming, walking or reading. Whatever it is, take some time out for yourself and don't restrict yourself to the identity of "the parent of the autistic child."

Mindfulness

Cognitive Behavioral Therapy (CBT), which includes mindfulness, is a set of exercises that can be practiced on one's own or facilitated by a therapist. It is a way of being kind to yourself and includes a deep focus on what may seem to be mundane. Don't rush things but rather observe the trees and flowers, their intricacies, and their beauty. When you sip your coffee, enjoy the sensory experience and focus only on that moment. The idea is to distract yourself from the stress of life in general by being present and giving your attention to what you are doing at that particular time. You can find guided mindfulness meditation on YouTube, Spotify, Apple Music, and many other platforms. These guided meditations involve relaxing music and a calming voice guiding you through close observation of your breathing, your wiggling toes, and other body sensations. I am not going to go into more detail, but I encourage readers to explore this avenue as a "me time" opportunity.

Challenges in Terms of Communication

Some youngsters who are neurodivergent have difficulty with verbal communication. Communication is a challenge for the parents of these children, which adds to the stress and anxiety that the parents already feel. The inability of their child to convey their requirements and preferences presents a barrier for the parents. The tribulations of parenting are made more difficult by the fact that youngsters do tend to struggle to read nonverbal communication and cues. As parents, we are aware of this, and being aware, in turn, empowers us to work on these difficulties with our children. Just a reminder that our autistic children are different. There is nothing "wrong" or "broken."

Stigmatization

There are many people on this planet, and therefore there are numerous responses to various scenarios and individuals. There are certain people who are not sensitive, compassionate, or accepting. The adverse reactions have a direct and personal influence on the child as well as on the parents, and unfortunately, the repercussions can last for some time. Breaking the stigma or at least making a dent in it can be done by raising awareness and getting people to start having conversations about autism. The three YouTube channels that I referred to earlier are doing just that, but it can be done on a much smaller scale. A short presentation at your child's school or an informative article in a local newspaper, in addition to encouraging friends and family to do their own research, all help.

How can parents efficiently face these challenges at home and enable their children to be comfortable? What better way to try to navigate these challenges than to take advice from and listen to the struggles of parents who have faced the same things?

raisingchildren.net.au created a video talking about the

various experiences of parents with children on the spectrum. Here are the comments from some of the parents in their own words.

Alison (mother of two children, including one Autistic child)

When you're battling with something you don't really understand, there's a huge learning curve, so a lot of the initial time is spent just trying to understand what's going on. Because I've got two children, we've got two children. You don't parent them the same. The way we parent our neurotypical daughter is very, very different from the way we parent Ellis. That was a huge learning curve because you can't parent them the same way. It doesn't work. And that's hard. Umm, people again cannot understand why it looks like you're letting him get away with things when you're really not.

Bobby (father of two children, including one autistic child)

There are a lot of challenges, challenges with his development, and challenges with his speech. How would he go to primary school? Would he be set back in certain situations? For example, if he gets bullied, would he be set back? And then all the work we've done won't be a waste but will be very disappointing because of something that's happening outside of our control. Our biggest challenges are just basically helping Peter become a little boy—a five-year-old little boy—that's like every other five-year-old little boy, who wants to just go out there and play and be accepted for who he is, not what he has.

Jane (mother of two children, including one Autistic child)

I think one of the hardest things is the fact that he doesn't enjoy people's company. I mean, we are social creatures, so it's really hard to see a child just want to be by themselves all the time.

Sharon (mother of two children, including one autistic child)

There was probably a period when Peter—the communication wasn't coming—and that was a really, really difficult period, so between two-and-a-half and three-and-a-half was probably the most turbulent year we'd had. Umm, because we didn't know what he wanted, how he wanted it when he wanted it. And that's where the PECs—the picture exchange cards – really helped and encouraged him to sort of make that initiation and that communication when it was something that he really wanted.

Shannon (father of four children, including three autistic children)

I'd like to be able to understand what Dominic's thinking when he's doing his really intense arm flaps—that's what the hardest thing is: We don't know why. He can be sitting here happy as anything, playing with his car, and the next thing his arms are going, and he's getting really intense. Before, it was just sort of his arms flapping [moves hands to demonstrate], but now he sort of twists his hand around and sort of moves his body [demonstrates with arm], and he goes really rigid. But when he's really involved in it, you can't get him out. You can see him try to break out of it, which is hard to see.

Marita (mother of two autistic children)

I think the most challenging thing is actually just all the little things you have to keep on top of. So, you have to remember what you're saying. Heidi, because of her sensory needs, she won't eat food that touches, so when I make macaroni and cheese for dinner, there's a bowl of macaroni, there's the cheese sauce, and then there are the vegetables. And she dips them into the cheese sauce, and it's all separate. And I have to remember these things, and if I accidentally make them together, it's a disaster. And having to remember the right toy to go to bed with or, you know, it's Tuesday. I need this special thing for school because it's Tuesday. The little things, they kind of buildup, and at the end of the week, I fall to pieces because I'm exhausted trying to remember it all through the week.

Joanne (mother of four children, including two autistic children)

The challenges I found, umm, even now, though my children are in school, the constant challenge is they're always behind. They're always behind academically, so you're always playing catch-up, so it's that constant "OK, what can I do next? How can I teach her to tell the time? How can I try and get her to tie her shoelaces?" And it's that you're always pushing. It keeps you awake at night; it keeps you awake at night as to "OK, what can I do now to help my child?"

Rachel (mother of four children, including three autistic children)

The biggest challenge, like for my personal challenge, is learning to pick and choose what is really relevant. So, I want to pick my battles and not sweat the small stuff, and spend my energy on the big stuff.

Joanne

There are extra financial burdens with special needs children. There's the fact that you ignore your husband more because you're spending so much time focusing on the children and their learning abilities. So, it's a lot more... harder on a marriage, yes. But we've hung in there [laughs].

Sharon

I guess it's really important that you make time as a couple. But sometimes it's not always possible. I mean, we're very lucky that my father-in-law and my mother-in-law are a great support network. Peter has sleepovers there all the time, so we get a respite in that respect. That's not a luxury that a lot of people have in our position. And, umm, but it's really important that we can just switch off because I think just as much as there is a risk of Peter being, if you like, over-therapized, and having everyday sort of, "What therapy do we need to be doing today?" Umm, I think he needs to have that level of non-structure, just as much as we need a relief or a break from the structured events in the day sometimes, just to let loose and do what we like.

Peter (father of two children, including one with Asperger's)

Get as much help as you can. Don't be afraid to ask. There's a lot of support out there, but you have to go and look for it. And you really have to, umm, where we were ten years ago—well, I suppose six, seven, eight years ago—I don't think there was that awareness that there is now. And it's much more prominent than it was. The avenues have opened up a little bit to access help, but you really still have to knock down doors, find individuals who will support you, and hang onto them, but just use every avenue that you've got to get help.

Marita

There are struggles; it's not always easy. But it's not always really hard, either. There are times when I just go, "That's amazing." We're walking down the street during Autumn, and the leaves are being blown out of the trees, and Heidi goes, "The leaves are pouring down." Because it looks like they're just being poured down, and that amazing way of seeing things so differently—I just love it.

Emotional Support for Parents

An important thing to recognize is that even superheroes sometimes require assistance, and there is absolutely no shame in that. To be able to provide a comfortable home environment for neurodivergent children, parents first need to make sure that their own mental health is in check, and research has shown time and again that parents who seek therapy often do better with their children.

In a recent study, a group of researchers came to the conclusion that parents who engage in cognitive therapy with their children who have autism also enjoy improvements in their own ability to regulate their moods and emotions. It is estimated that over 70percent of children with autism struggle with emotional or behavioral issues. These children may benefit from cognitive behavior therapy to enhance their capacity to control their emotions and improve their overall functioning.

The researchers came to the conclusion that parents who take part in cognitive treatment with their children also enjoy a genuine advantage that contributes to an enhanced quality of life for the entire family. "When parents bring their children in for cognitive behavior therapy, the vast majority of the time, they are shown to a separate room where they are educated on what their children are doing, and they are not considered to be co-therapists. What we found to be particularly interesting about our research is the dynamic that emerges when parents are actively involved in all stages of the process. We are now able to demonstrate that it is beneficial for the parents of children diagnosed with autism, in addition to the fact that it is beneficial for the children themselves." said Jonathan Weiss, Ph.D., a CIHR Chair in Autism Spectrum Disorders (ASD) Treatment and Care Research. in addition to being an Associate Professor in the Department of Psychology in the Faculty of Health (Weiss, 2017).

Therapy is beneficial for autistic children, but it also has a significant positive impact on the parents. In a recent study, a group of researchers came to the conclusion that parents who engage in cognitive therapy with their children who have autism also enjoy improvements in their own ability to regulate their moods and emotions. It is estimated that over 70percent of autistic children struggle with emotional or behavioral issues. These children may benefit from cognitive behavior therapy to enhance their capacity to control their emotions and improve their overall functioning.

The parents who participated in the study were given the opportunity to take part in a controlled random experiment. They were asked to fill out surveys both before and after the treatment, and their responses were compared to those of parents who had not yet started therapy. During the course of a trial of cognitive behavior therapy for children with autism spectrum disorder (ASD) aged 8 to 12 who did not have an intellectual disability, Weiss and Ph.D. student Andrea Maughan investigated how parents' mental health, mindfulness, and perceptions of their children changed over the course of the study.

For the purposes of the study, parents were given the role of co-therapists with the professional who was treating their children, and they were tasked with implementing the same tactics alongside their children. Because of this, the parents were able to learn how to assist themselves throughout the procedure. During the activities, parents were obligated to keep a journal of their children's ideas and reactions. "As a parent who took part in the SAS:

OR Program, I experienced the same level of personal development as my child did. With my son, I used to employ a strategy of "one size fits all;" now, both he and I have various tools at our disposal to help us navigate through challenging situations. Our lives have been enriched with positivity and comfort as a result of our ability to communicate our feelings, recognize triggers, and think proactively about potential ways. According to Jessica Jannarone, a mother who participated in the research project, the most meaningful part of her involvement was "seeing my child mature in this program and finding a method to start handling his feelings."

According to the findings of the study, when parents participated in cognitive therapy with their children, they saw changes in their own levels of sadness, as well as in their ability to regulate their emotions and be more mindful parents. It helped them become more aware of their parenting and all of the good they do as parents, which is something that helped them become more aware of their parenting and all of the good they do as parents. The research showed that parents improved their abilities to handle their own emotions and to see themselves in a more positive light.

The findings of this study also highlight how important it is for healthcare practitioners to involve the child's parents in the process of providing care to the child when the child has autism. Weiss summed up his findings by stating in the conclusion that "we know that parents of children with autism endure substantial levels of distress in addition to all of the wonderful experiences they have." Therefore, if there is anything that can be done to lessen that, we have an obligation to make an effort to do so. The findings of the study were presented in an article that was published in the Journal of Autism and Developmental Disorders.

This study, and many more, continue to shed light on exactly how important it is for parents to seek therapy alongside their children. You know what they say on all of our flights, put your own oxygen mask on before helping others.

Chapter 8

Growing Pains

Researchers are just starting to understand what goes on in the brains of Neurodivergent children during the adolescent years to explain the distinct social, cognitive, and emotional issues that these individuals face.

For Neurodivergent children and adolescents, puberty can be a very trying time. As neurodivergent people age sexually and become more eager in friendships and relationships, it can be difficult for them to cope with the symptoms of autism, which include difficulties with sensory and emotional processing, actions that are repetitive, and a lack of social nuance. As a result of their inability to comprehend the complexities of the relationships between neurotypical girls, neurodivergent girls may have an especially difficult time interacting socially. One study conducted in 2006 found that 72 percent of 109 autistic children experienced depression, anxiety, or another mental health issue. Eating disorders are also uncommonly widespread in autistic adolescents. Comparatively, a survey conducted in 2016 on more than 50,000 neurotypical children and adolescents found that fewer than 20% of them suffer from a mental health disorder (Magnuson, 2016).

In the meantime, the process of quicker long-distance signaling in the brain occurs during adolescence. This occurs as bundles of nerve fibers grow coated in fatty insulation, thus forming new neural highways. This remodeling of the brain usually results in increased cognitive abilities, such as improved problem-solving, as well as emotional maturity and a heightened sense of identity. And despite the fact that many young people on the spectrum exhibit comparable improvement, there is a sizable population that does not.

Although puberty has been compared to a roller coaster, it is a slow and bumpy ride. It manifests itself in stages and entails profound alterations to the structure and function of the brain. During this period of time, the brain eliminates any neural connections (synapses) that were created during the first ten to fifteen years of life but were never utilized. Before adolescence, the areas of the brain that are responsible for basic sensory and motor processes begin to undergo pruning. The dorsolateral prefrontal cortex, which is involved in higher cognitive tasks such as impulse control, decision-making, judgment, social skills, and emotional regulation, is one of the areas that are among the last to undergo this maturation process.

Growing up autistic or neurodivergent can be a challenging but ultimately rewarding experience for the individual. Autistic adolescents with ASD may have difficulties forming relationships, which is one of the challenges they confront. Because it can be challenging to interpret nonverbal clues such as body language, it can be challenging to take part in conversations or to build friendships with other people.

On the other hand, many autistic adolescents are exceptionally knowledgeable and provide fresh points of view on the world. They may be exceptionally gifted in the areas of music or art, or they may excel in academics.

Neurodiverse adolescents and their families may face a number of challenges as they navigate the complexities of growing up. Finding a method of communication that is both efficient and successful is one of the most difficult difficulties. Because many neurodiverse adolescents are nonspeaking, it can be challenging for them to communicate their requirements and preferences. Frustration and other behavioral problems may result from this. In addition, having trouble communicating might make it difficult to interact with other people and form connections with them.

However, there are many things that one can do to smooth out the transition period from childhood to adolescence.

- Build a solid foundation: Start early and build a strong foundation of communication skills, including nonverbal communication strategies such as gestures, pictures, or communication devices.

- Develop coping skills: Adolescence can be a time of heightened stress, so it's important to develop coping skills for you and your child. For example, practice relaxation techniques and identify trusted individuals who can provide support.

- Encourage self-expression: Help your child find ways to express themselves, such as through art, music, or writing. This can also help develop communication skills.

- Foster independence: Encourage your child's independence by gradually increasing their responsibilities and practicing hygiene, dressing, and meal preparation skills.

- Develop a transition plan: Develop a transition plan that outlines the goals and objectives for your child during adolescence. This can include educational, vocational, and independent living goals.

- Stay connected: Connect with your child's healthcare providers, educators, and community resources. Seek support from other parents going through similar experiences, and consider joining a support group.

Foster Independence

Your adolescent with neurodivergence will benefit much from your assistance in cultivating autonomous abilities that will serve them well as they enter adulthood. This could entail things like cooking, cleaning, making a budget, and figuring out how to get around using public transit.

A Neurodiversity-affirming Approach to Social Skills

As we know, neurodiversity is the idea that autistic

individuals have differences and not deficits. Ableist language refers to the language used when referring to a disability as something negative. We know that being autistic is not being disabled, but words or phrases like "dumb," "I'm OCD," and "special needs" are offensive and can lead to those awful feelings of isolation. Basically, we need to focus on differences and the positive side of those differences.

We don't want to teach neurodiverse children to imitate neurotypical social skills. This can cause the neurodiverse child to learn to "mask." Masking is harmful to the ND person. For example, typical social skills training goals often attempt to minimize the appearance of autistic characteristics to get someone to blend in, which is harmful to self-esteem and identity.

Start Preparing for Adjustments

The teenage years are, at times, marked by both significant and subtle life shifts. Discussing these upcoming shifts in advance can be of great assistance to your autistic adolescent's preparation for them. It's possible that this will help you feel more in control of your life and less anxious. Encourage them to take part in the planning process and present them with options that will empower them whenever you can.

Encourage Good Self-Esteem

It is critical for a neurodivergent to have a positive self-image and sense of accomplishment. Praise your adolescent child's abilities and acknowledge their achievements to encourage the development of a healthy, positive self-image in them. Take pictures of meaningful events so that you can celebrate accomplishments and commemorate reaching personal milestones in a way that your child may enjoy.

How to Deal with the Adolescent Period When Your Child is Neurodivergent

The adolescent years can be difficult for anybody, but for people with neurodivergence, the move into puberty can have a significant and devastating influence on their lives. Autistic teenagers frequently have to contend with increased anxiety and heightened sensitivity to sensory input. This is in addition to the normal physical and hormonal changes that all teenagers go through. As a consequence of this, they could have difficulties at school, in their communities, and in communicating with other people.

There are, nevertheless, steps that can be taken to make the transition into neurodivergent adolescence less challenging. One method is therapy, which focuses on providing patients with positive reinforcement and instructing them in new skills in manageable increments. Finding an experienced therapist who is also autistic and understands the condition is essential. Teenagers who have autism are capable of overcoming the particular difficulties that come with being on the spectrum if they have the appropriate support system in place.

In addition, parents and other carers can lend support and understanding while also assisting in the establishment of reasonable boundaries and objectives for their children. Parents and other carers can assist in making the transition into adulthood easier for neurodiverse individuals and their families if they take the appropriate supportive actions throughout this time of life.

Giving Teenagers the Words

Self-advocacy is the ability to speak up for oneself and communicate one's needs and desires. It's an essential skill for all teenagers, but particularly important for autistic teenagers with unique needs and challenges.

Self-advocacy can help autistic teenagers take ownership of their lives and advocate for accommodations and support they need to succeed. It can also help them build confidence, improve self-esteem, and develop essential life skills.

However, many autistic teenagers may struggle with self-advocacy due to communication challenges. They may not know how to express their needs or feel uncomfortable speaking up for themselves.

Helping Autistic Teenagers Find Their Voice

There are several strategies that parents, teachers, and caregivers can use to help autistic teenagers find their voice and develop self-advocacy skills:

Encourage Communication: It's essential to create

a supportive environment where autistic teenagers feel comfortable expressing themselves. Encourage communication in all forms, including verbal, written, and nonverbal. Our ability to handle comfort and confidence is made MUCH more straightforward when we encourage them to communicate about things they love and care about. Think about it this way, if you lived in a world where people wanted to share about something that didn't interest you all the time, you might want to communicate less. But if you had a few good friends who you shared interests with, you would be MUCH more likely to share your thoughts and feelings with them.

Practice Social Communication Skills: Social communication skills can be practiced and developed. Encourage autistic teenagers to practice initiating conversations, taking turns, and reading nonverbal cues with people they are comfortable with-not strangers.

Use Visual Supports: Visual supports such as pictures, symbols, and social stories can be helpful for autistic teenagers who struggle with communication. They can provide a visual cue for communication and help understand social situations.

Teach Self-Advocacy Skills: Autistic teenagers can learn self-advocacy skills through modeling and practice. Encourage them to speak up (it doesn't have to be verbal; they can send an email.) for themselves and provide opportunities to practice these skills in real-life situations.

Advocate for Accommodations: Parents, teachers, and caregivers can help autistic teenagers advocate for extra time on tests, preferential seating, and sensory support. These accommodations can help level the playing field and make it easier for autistic teenagers to communicate and learn.

Remember, their lives will likely change toward the end of their teen years as high school will end, and they may get a job, go to college, or start their own business. Prepare them as best as possible by teaching them what the world expects of them. Let them then decide how to proceed and when to communicate with others.

Learning in Tragedy

The stories above conjure different emotions and illustrate parental emotions too. As parents, we are always learning, but we need the assistance of teachers and therapists because at home, sometimes "normal" is not enough. Recently I came to identify something I already knew, but on a bigger level, while watching a Netflix documentary called American Tragedy. The parent of one of the Columbine shooters, Sue Klebold, was interviewed. It was surprising to learn how "normal" her son Dylan Klebold's

life was before the shooting. He went to prom, his parents were married, and he had a rich life that involved hobbies and celebrations. As I watched and listened with an open mind, I wholeheartedly believed his mother when she spoke about the genuine shock of learning from the shooting. The disbelief and horror in her eyes and heart were palpable. When she talked about her relationship with her son, she said something to the effect of, this wasn't a child that was ignored or neglected; I was that mom who grabbed his face and looked him in the eyes and told him he was loved and that I was proud of him, on a more regular basis than most parents do! Mrs. Klebold understands teenagers more now than she did then. She acknowledges that there were conversations that they didn't have about thoughts and feelings. The documentary's takeaway was that the most effective approaches for social and emotional learning should be integrated into school curriculums and provide skill building across all grade levels to reach all children. The best social and emotional learning efforts are proactive, not reactive. That means we don't wait for problems to come up to deal with them. Instead, we prevent problems through our word choice. As a society, we want to ensure children cannot only recognize emotions and feelings but also give words to them.

Communication With an Autistic Partner

Be Clear and Direct: When communicating with an autistic partner, it's essential to be clear and direct. Avoid using figurative language, sarcasm, or indirect communication. Instead, use clear, concise language and express your needs and expectations.

Use Visual Supports: Visual supports such as pictures, diagrams, and written instructions can be helpful for autistic individuals who struggle with verbal communication. Use visual supports to supplement oral communication and provide additional cues for understanding.

Avoid Overstimulation: Autistic individuals may be

sensitive to sensory input such as bright lights, loud noises, and certain textures. Avoid overstimulation during communication by creating a calm, quiet environment and minimizing distractions.

Practice Active Listening: Active listening involves paying attention to the speaker and providing feedback to show that you understand what they are saying. Practice active listening by repeating back what your partner has said, clarifying any misunderstandings, and asking questions for clarification.

Respect Differences: Autistic individuals may have different communication styles and preferences than neurotypical individuals. Respect these differences by acknowledging and valuing their unique perspective.

Create a Communication Plan: Creating a communication plan with your autistic partner can help establish clear expectations and boundaries around communication. This plan can include preferred modes of communication, strategies for managing misunderstandings, and guidelines for avoiding overstimulation.

Communication is essential to any successful relationship, but it can be particularly challenging when one or both partners are autistic. By understanding communication challenges and using clear and direct communication, visual supports, active listening, and respect for differences, we can improve communication in a relationship with an autistic person. It's important to remember that communication is a two-way street and that both partners must be willing to listen and adapt to build a robust and healthy relationship.

As a speech-language pathologist, I have worked with several children who struggle with selective mutism. Unfortunately, this condition is often misunderstood, and many people do not realize its impact on a child's life.

Selective mutism is a complex disorder that affects a child's ability to speak in certain situations, even though they may be perfectly capable of speaking in others. This condition is not simply shyness or a reluctance to say; it is a natural and severe disorder that can significantly impact a child's social and academic development.

The causes of selective mutism are not fully understood, but it is believed to be related to anxiety and fear. Children with selective mutism may fear social situations, such as school or public places, and feel overwhelmed by the pressure to speak. They may also have experienced trauma or other underlying anxiety disorders contributing to their inability to speak.

When working with children with selective mutism, it is essential to approach treatment gently and patiently. The goal of treatment is to gradually increase the child's comfort level in speaking, so they can communicate more freely in all situations.

One of the most effective treatments for selective mutism is cognitive behavioral therapy (CBT). This therapy helps children identify their fears and anxieties and develop coping strategies. For example, a child may learn relaxation techniques, such as deep breathing or visualization, to help them manage their stress in social situations.

Another important aspect of treatment is socialization. Children with selective mutism may feel isolated and disconnected from their peers, worsening their anxiety. Socialization therapy helps children develop social skills and build relationships with their peers in a safe and supportive environment.

As a speech-language pathologist, my role in treating selective mutism is to help children improve their communication skills and develop strategies for overcoming their anxiety. This may involve working on specific speech and language goals, such as enhancing articulation, expanding vocabulary, and addressing the underlying anxiety causing selective mutism.

Selective mutism is a challenging disorder, but with the proper treatment and support, children can learn to communicate more effectively and overcome their fears.

This disorder is often observed in children and adults. Individuals may consistently fail to speak in social situations even though they can do so in other contexts. Children with ASD who experience SM may find it particularly challenging to communicate with others and express themselves effectively, leading to developmental difficulties.

Selective mutism in children often presents as a consistent failure to speak in social situations such as school or play dates, where the child is expected to interact with others.

Children with this condition may communicate effectively at home or with close family members but become silent in unfamiliar social settings. As a result, their ability to build social connections may be affected, and their academic progress may also suffer.

The root causes of selective mutism in children are still not fully understood. However, it is believed to result from the complex interaction of genetic, environmental, and neurodevelopmental factors. Children with ASD who experience SM may be prone to social anxiety, making it challenging to communicate with others. The fear of negative evaluation or social judgment may further exacerbate their symptoms.

Selective mutism in children requires a multidisciplinary approach to treatment. Therapies such as cognitive-behavioral therapy (CBT) and speech therapy can help children overcome their social anxiety and learn to communicate effectively in different social situations. Parents and caregivers can also play a critical role in providing support and creating a supportive environment for the child. In some cases, medication may also be prescribed to manage anxiety symptoms.

SM can significantly impact a child's social, emotional, and academic development. Early identification and appropriate intervention can make a substantial difference in helping children overcome their communication challenges and improve their quality of life.

Some Words of Wisdom for the Parents of Neurodivergent Adolescents

When it comes to parenting a neurodivergent adolescent, there are a few essential things that every parent ought to keep in mind. To begin, it is essential to keep in mind that autism is a disorder that exists on a spectrum. This indicates that no two people who have autism are exactly the same as one another. Therefore, what is effective for one neurodiverse person might not be effective for another.

Second, do not be reluctant to ask for assistance from qualified individuals. There are a great number of therapists and counselors that focus their practices on dealing with adolescents on the autism spectrum and the families of those adolescents. Finally, make sure to retain an open line of communication with your teenager. It is necessary to grasp their perspective by letting them know you are there for them. This may not be a simple task, but it is essential to do so. You can be of great assistance to your
teenager who has autism by following these straightforward recommendations and putting them into practice.

Neurodivergence Can be a Strength

When caring for an adolescent who is neurodivergent, it is important to understand the particular strengths that separate them apart from their friends who are neurotypical. There are many ways in which having can be beneficial, despite the fact that the condition presents its own unique set of difficulties in certain areas. People with autism, for instance, have the propensity to be extremely honest and to possess a robust sense of fairness. They frequently have a remarkable capacity for learning and recalling information.

Additionally, autistic people typically have an exceptional capacity for focus and attention to detail in their daily lives. They can build off of these strengths to improve their performance in school and in the occupations they pursue in the future. For instance, if they are trustworthy and have a strong desire to see justice done, they can choose a career as a lawyer or an advocate for social reform. If they are exceptionally smart and have excellent memories, they may pursue careers as physicians or scientists.

There is no upper limit to what a teenager who is neurodivergent is capable of doing in their lifetime. The important thing is to acknowledge each person's distinctive qualities and work to their benefit. They have the potential to accomplish everything they set their minds to if they put in the effort. However, there needs to be some form of control in the age of ease of information and online presence.

Marc Brackett, the Permission to Feel author, mentioned previously, says that 45percent of teenagers are online almost constantly. They spend about six hours a day on social media or surfing the internet; when people spend more time on screens, they have less time to do the things that are important to them, like thinking about their feelings. What further complicates things is that when emotionally immature parents don't know how to handle their children's emotions, they frequently take them personally. They punish their children for feeling undesirable and make them feel ashamed for feeling them instead of helping them deal with them (Brackett, 2019).

The Negative Effects of Social Media on Autistic Teenagers

Social media has more negative than positive elements, no matter who you are. The dangers of sexual grooming, indoctrination, and manipulation are constantly there. Statistics show that approximately 37percent of 12 to 17-year-olds globally have been victims of cyberbullying (Atske, 2022). It is no coincidence that teen suicides have become troublingly frequent in the social media age and that emotional intelligence can be stunted by excessive screen time.

The good news is that autistic teenagers spend less time on social media compared with their neurotypical counterparts. Studies have shown that 13.2 percent of autistic teenagers use social media. It is the responsibility of parents and teachers to explain the dangers of social media to teenagers, including the disconnect from reality. It isn't all bad, though. YouTube, for instance, which isn't based on direct interaction, has some really good channels run by autistic individuals that can be used to develop and understand how others feel emotions. Some of my favorites are as follows:

- The Aspie World www.youtube.com/@ TheAspieWorld

- Autism from the Inside www.youtube.com/watch?v=A9nDmiYUSlA

- Yo Samdy Sam www.youtube.com/watch?v=pMx1DnSn-eg

The Significance of Having Many Support Systems Available When One is a Teenager

Autistic teens have access to a wide variety of support networks that can assist them in navigating the difficulties that may arise as they mature. Teenagers who participate in these programs may develop the skills necessary to achieve academic and personal success. Teenagers with autism are able to conquer obstacles and be active members of their communities if they have access to the appropriate support systems, for instance:

- Center for Autism and Related Disorders

    centerforautism.com

- Key Autism Services

    www.keyautismservices.com/

- Step Ahead ABA

    nc.stepaheadaba.com/

Chapter 9

Listen to the Words (or Lack Thereof)

We communicate so that we may be understood, so that our needs can be supported, so that we can ask for directions, so that we can describe, and even so that we can share a memory with someone we care about. As technologies and gadgets that can facilitate alterations to the ways in which we communicate become more widely available, there are now more methods than ever before to communicate. Some people write, some people sign, and some people use tools.

Communication is NOT acquired language, nor is it speech; rather, it is the means by which we attain comprehension as well as the speech that we use. In addition to this, it enables social contact.

There is always a combination of verbal communication, non-verbal communication, and both in every interaction. Our daily interactions consist of approximately 80 percent non-verbal communication and 20 percent verbal communication. This is due to the fact that we communicate with one another through the movements and postures of our bodies, the expressions on our faces, the intonation of our voices, and the noises we make. Non-verbal learning disability, or NVLD, is a condition that affects some people and makes it challenging for them to speak or interact as successfully as others.

Non-Verbal Autism

Statistics show that about 40percent of autistic individuals are completely non-verbal. That leaves a 60% quotient, many of whom are partially verbal and partially non-verbal, which means that understanding your child's communication style is vitally important.

Communication is essential for any person providing care. Speech is the primary mode of communication used by most people and may tell you everything from whether or not your child is hungry to whether or not they are upset. On the other hand, some children who have autism spectrum disorder (ASD) do not speak at all. However, this does not imply that they are unable to communicate or that they are not interested in doing so. People who have ASD still have the same goals as everyone else when it comes to expressing their thoughts and feelings. Still, they do so through gestures, sounds, and other forms of nonverbal communication.

Autism without verbal symptoms is not a recognized diagnostic category. People who are diagnosed with autism spectrum disorder (ASD) and never learn to speak more than a few words are referred to by this subcategory of the disorder. It is estimated that forty percent of those diagnosed with ASD are nonverbal.

The condition known as severe autism, also referred to as level 3 autism, is typically associated with the presence of nonverbal autism. A child may eventually develop the ability to communicate verbally in certain circumstances. New methods of treatment and technological advancements are making it feasible for children who have autism to communicate in various ways, even if they do not speak.

Level 3 autism is typically associated with the presence of nonverbal autism. However, a child may eventually develop the ability to communicate verbally in certain circumstances. In addition, new treatment methods and technological advancements are making it feasible for children who have autism to communicate in various ways, even if they do not speak.

So Then, How Do These Non-Verbal Individuals Communicate?

Many parents of non-speakers can tell you the signs of enthusiasm that a non-speaker is experiencing, as well as the instances that signal sadness, anguish, or frustration. It is more challenging to learn an autistic person's body language because it is not invariably typical of other people's body language. We must refrain from attributing a lack of intelligence or ability to non-speakers just because they do not speak and appear disinterested in connections with others. Non-speakers may not be able to convey that their ear has been hurting for several hours or what they think of the characters in their favorite stories. This is why the exploration of AAC is so important. You may wonder why a child doesn't just point to their ear if they are non-speaking and they are experiencing pain in the ear. We must remember that the neurodivergent mind does not work in the same way as a neurotypical mind. Sometimes those differences do not allow someone to make the connections needed to indicate something like an earache. Sometimes, it could be that their interoceptive sense does not function properly. Sometimes, they are unable to formulate their thoughts into words, so they may not be thinking in language or pictures. Therefore, they cannot come up with a way to indicate ear pain. As a caregiver, we must be highly astute to subtle changes that may occur in the moods and behaviors of non-speaking individuals.

It is worth noting that several non-speaking people do not yet have access to communication. Some parents and family members have exhausted all possible options but have not discovered anything their child can use to communicate in a practical setting. This circumstance can be a heartbreaking experience for both the autistic person and their family. Some people do not have the financial means to investigate alternative approaches. Some people may be unaware of the available choices. Even if their child expresses their affection for them in other ways, the words "I love you" are the only thing that some parents and families want to hear from their child.

"And sometimes, just sometimes, we are comfortable in our silence and not interested in communicating, even if we have a way to communicate" (Mahler, 2020).

Are non-verbal autistic people not physically able to speak, or is it more a choice not to speak? I'm ignorant about this and would like to know more.

"Neither. I've experienced selective mutism a few times. Your ability to form words is just gone. During one episode, even though I couldn't talk, I could still make sounds and answer yes or no questions with "mm hm, mm mm." But even that was hard.

There are all these thoughts in your brain that you want to get out of. But you just can't parse them into words. I've had other episodes where when I talked, it was practically nonsense. The words all jumbled together in my head, trying to make sense of abstract concepts. I'm even confused by the words that come out. I guess it makes sense because autistic brains tend not to have differentiation between hemispheres. Abstract and linear thinking are mixed together.

Neurotypicals can shift between abstract and linear thinking (their default state is linear thinking). It's one or the other thing. Autistic people don't switch hemispheres. The whole brain swings from linear to abstract and areas in between. Abstract thinking is also linked with emotional processing, which makes sense because selective mutism is often triggered by strong emotions.

When it comes to completely nonverbal autistics, I think there's more going on than that. Some of them are able to formulate their thoughts into words using alternative communication devices, writing, sign language, etc. So, they are able to think linearly. They can usually still make sounds. But the ability to formulate words just isn't there.

I was nonverbal until I was four. It took the help of a speech therapist to get me to talk. Some autistic people have no speech delays. Some can overcome speech issues with help. Some never do. The inability to speak has nothing to do with intelligence or physical issues. It's a processing error. Either internally (abstract thought process) or in networking (the speech center of the brain's control over the mouth)" (Grimm, n.d.).

www.quora.com/Can-someone-who-isnt-autistic-go-non-verbal

Visual Tools

Spoken language can prove challenging to children, even if they are not non-speaking communicators. Remember that putting words into meaning during a conversation or describing how a situation made a child feel is often something that doesn't come easily. The story of Aiden and describing an occurrence as his "brain being on crack" in chapter 1 is a good example of this. He was unable to ask to be excused because he didn't have the words. Aiden had never been taught the words to use to make

an exit in those circumstances, as well as the words necessary to describe what he was experiencing. As I said, I spent the session that followed giving Aiden the words and the following visual tools are ones that can help in preparing autistic children for similar experiences.

Creating Gantt Charts

These can be found online, but to briefly explain, Gantt charts show activities against time. Kind of like a bar chart with time vertically and the task (a science class, let's say) horizontally. This provides a visual representation of a schedule. You can access all the information on Gantt. com.

Social Stories

Carol Gray, a multiple award-winning autism consultant, is responsible for the creation of Carol Gray Social Stories ©. In 1989, Carol began writing stories for her autistic students within the Michigan-based Jenison Public School Group and noted great results in coping with day-to-day life, including a vast array of interactions.

Unplanned events can happen and may be challenging to deal with. Preparing your child for the unexpected via social stories can be an excellent tool to increase communication and decrease anxiety.

Stories and drawings can be simple but powerful. You don't have to be an artist to write a social story for your child.

Go right ahead and make stick figures and a simple bus to tell a story about how sometimes people get sick. For example, the usual driver is sick today, so Ms. Holly is helping drive the children on the school bus until Ms. Brenda feels better. When Ms. Brenda is better, she will drive the bus again.

Timers

I'm sure your first thought was "hourglass," and if so, you would be correct. You could also use a "Time Timer," which is a battery-operated clock-type machine that represents time in one-hour passages. The website, www. timetimer.com/, offers reasonably priced timers and a range of other time-keeping products.

Picture Cards

Just like neurotypicals respond to picture cards, autistic children do the same. Cast your mind back to the picture of the cat, with the word "cat" written below it. There are apps and devices that offer digital picture cards, but I prefer the old-school type of cards!

Video-Based Teaching

TV can be a great teacher as long as the material is educational but also enjoyable for the child. Learning when it is appropriate to use certain phrases and respond to social cues can be conveyed well by video. Internalization of content by repetition, as well as the combination of verbal and visual content, can be attributed to this type of learning.

Video Modeling

The idea of video modeling is to show rather than tell, and it involves two facets. Firstly, there are specifically acted videos, and secondly, there are videos made in class, therapy, or at the home of the child and their behaviors. This teaching technique focuses on body language and facial expressions. As before, children can have trouble identifying when empathy is required, and the advantage that video modeling has over static content is that videos are more realistic in terms of showing what others are feeling. The same applies to the "unwritten" social rules that are kind of "just there" in society, which are better displayed via video, as opposed to static images.

Video Previews

If you go to a theme park or a zoo, to use an example, there are often induction-type videos that are shown to school groups as preparation for the upcoming experience. The same can be applied in therapy, at school, or at home for the same preparatory purposes.

Emotional Intelligence and Learning

Verywellmind.com defines emotional intelligence as "the ability to perceive, interpret, demonstrate, control, evaluate, and use emotions to communicate with and relate to others effectively and constructively."

The above can be read as a list of skills that children lack, but fortunately, emotional intelligence can be taught, although it remains difficult to learn. The premise is based on the Theory of Mind, which hypothesizes that the better you are at imagining or seeing the world from another person's perspective, the better you are at displaying emotional intelligence (The Family Guidance and Therapy Center, 2022). But before we get to that point, it is important to educate our children about their own emotions. It is difficult to learn emotional intelligence without the foundation of the basics of emotions and how they manifest on a child-to-child basis. As a parent, there are a few things you can do to achieve this.

Acknowledge and Label

If your child has a meltdown, there is little that you can do at the time. However, at a later stage, you can have a question-and-answer session, where you allow your child to describe how they felt. From that point, you can attach a label to the emotion. There are several benefits for the child, including developing the ability to identify AND name the emotions in others.

Encourage Expression of Emotions

Can you imagine if we all suppressed our emotions? The world would be a melting pot ready to explode. Different emotions are displayed differently by different people, and we need to convey to our children that it is okay to experience the feelings they are having. The next step is to suggest and give examples of alternative outlets, as well as social situations during which one should not act on an emotion. It is "socially inappropriate" to get angry and punch someone in the face, but many adults do it anyway. The point is that it can be very difficult to refrain from acting on a negative emotion, and children must be made aware of the difficulty. Acceptance of emotions and feelings, leading to regulation, is the end goal. Don't forget to let your child know that they are not being judged and must not judge themselves.

Listen

We all sometimes need someone to just listen, free of judgment, criticism, and distraction; it helps us to let go of things and move on. Teachers, therapists, and parents need to create a non-judgmental atmosphere and pay 100percent attention to what the child wants to say. There doesn't need to be a set time for this, but making observations and basing questions on the observations can encourage a child to talk. Here are a few suggestions on how

to use language correctly to facilitate an environment where you become a listener (as a parent):

- It looks like something is bothering you. You know that's okay, right? I'm here if you'd like to talk about it, but it's completely fine if you don't.

- Some days I get frustrated at work. Do you ever get frustrated?

- You seem really happy! Would you like to tell me about things that make you feel happy?

The third example is probably the easiest, but it's all about making the child feel comfortable talking, knowing that you will listen without distraction.

Roleplay and Problem-Solving

Feelings and emotions can be better understood through roleplay, which leads to problem-solving in the sense of dealing with emotions. Sharing is a good example, and can be addressed through a role-play exercise where you, as a parent, act like you have a toy that you don't want to share. Your child can be given the role of asking if they can play with your toy, and you can explain that the right thing to do is to say "Yes," and encourage sharing.

Now What?

Well, you now have the knowledge, understanding, methods, and a manual, in the form of this book, to do the best you can do to give your child the words and the actions (in the case of non-verbal autism). All these methods create greater knowledge and understanding, which leads to the identification of similar emotions within others, and emotional intelligence is allowed to develop.

Conclusion

It would be safe to say that if you have reached this point, then you are in a more educated position on children and the importance of giving them words. Below is a consolidated recap that can be used as a set of reference points to go back to areas that were particularly informative and that you, the reader, have identified with.

Children can struggle to find the words to express their feelings, and a case in point is that of Aiden and the sensory overload that he experienced but was unable to react verbally at the time. Don't forget that naming emotions is useful in creating understanding. If a child expresses anger without understanding what the emotion actually is but is taught what it is through roleplay and assigning the correct word, then steps are being taken to give the words to that child.

As we now know, there are eight senses as opposed to five, and the processing of sensory information either prevents children from or encourages them to adapt to their environments. Take note of the story of Jayden in chapter two and how his sensory overload created dysregulation. Basically, Jayden was bombarded by sensory unpleasantness from the moment that he woke up until he became so dysregulated that he punched another child at his school.

Although difficult to control, there are sensory devices that can be used to mitigate dysregulation. For example, lava lamps for sight sensitivity or weighted blankets for touch seekers. When used in conjunction with exercises, such as swimming or bike riding, for improved spatial awareness of proprioception deficiency or obstacle courses for interoception difficulties.

Just like sense, there are eight components to communication, very briefly summarized below:

- Source: Choosing the correct selection of words to convey meaning.

- Message: Conveying the meaning via the selected words/even actions.

- Channel: Talking, writing, even drawing.

- Receiver: The person receiving and interpreting the message.

- Feedback: Display of how accurately the message has been interpreted.

- Environment: The environment in which you communicate.

- Context: Casual context, such as on the beach, or less casual, say during therapy.

- Interference: Exterior factors such as background noise or uncomfortable lighting.

On the subject of learning, there are many methods, some of which overlap. However, certain categories are commonly acknowledged. Visual or spatial learners benefit from flashcards, schedules, sketching, and videos. Auditory exercises include using music or filmed lectures to teach. These are suited to autistic listeners. Role play and group discussion suit linguistic learners best, especially involving reading and writing. In addition, you get social, physical, natural, and logical learners, as explained in chapter three.

Following on from the different types of learning, there are also language processing differences. Because children are often more literal than adults, they often gravitate towards analytical language processing, which is a logical breaking down of the language. Then you have Gestalt language processing, where the meaning of the language is discerned as a whole, meaning that there is less focus on every single word.

Echolalia, being the repetition of words or sentences heard from others, can be related to both types of language processing and in certain instances, can be problematic. As I have mentioned, repetition is the basis for learning anything. However, when it is unfounded or excessive, then speech therapy should be considered. Explaining visual and verbal cues, as well as positive reinforcement, are also means to treat echolalia.

All children deserve to have access to education, but it isn't always that easy because of alternative needs. The Individuals with Disabilities Education Act (IDEA) is the legislation that facilitates free education appropriate to children with disabilities. Even though autism is not a disability, it falls under the auspices of the act, which is a good thing in that it upholds the rights of autistic children to receive an appropriate education. The downside is that sensory integration therapy is not always seen as educationally relevant. However, there does seem to be a shift away from this mindset, and it is books like this that need to create awareness on the subject to assist in this mindset change.

Broadly speaking, there are several ways to promote learning in the visual sense. Some examples are Gantt charts, picture cards, and video-based teaching, as explored in chapter six. The use of social stories under the umbrella of the Carol Gray Social Stories © brand has proven successful in teaching autistic children how to cope in situations that are the same or similar to what they have read or listened to. Emotional intelligence is a set of skills that can be honed via social stories and can be explained as part of the theory of mind. In short, when children can see, interpret and understand another person's point of view, then they can identify with that person in an emotionally intelligent way.

In terms of understanding, children should be taught how to acknowledge an emotion, put a name to it, and not be ashamed to display that emotion, BUT not in ways that are harmful to others. We can achieve this by listening to what our children have to say through open-ended questions and giving them the option to start a discussion or not. Initiating these conversations should be done in a comfortable environment, non-intrusively and non-judgmentally.

Referring back to Marc Brackett's book, Permission to Feel, there are judgmental parents out there. Don't be one! Also, don't be a parent that allows free reign in terms of access to social media. The statistics, as discussed in chapter six, are alarming, and it is a parental duty to explain the dangers of social media to your children, autistic or not. Having said that, there are positives and learning facilities through the YouTube channels that I mentioned, among others. Either way, you need to be proactive and not reactive.

In chapter seven, we looked at the way in which children are influenced by the experiences that happen at home. Apart from the constant love and support that parents of autistic children (all children) need to provide, the home can be set up in such a way as to create a comfortable environment. This involves catering to sensory needs in such a way as to allow your child to be him or herself. Assistance in understanding and encouraging communication, verbal or otherwise, that meets the needs of your child goes a long way to establishing that comfort. There will undoubtedly be challenges and tough days, but you, as a parent, need to be kind to yourself when you can. We all need emotional support at times, so don't be hesitant to reach out when you need it, and don't be afraid to break out of the identity mold as the parent of an autistic child.

Find time for the things you love. Whether you enjoy exercising, swimming, reading, or whatever, allow yourself to enjoy those activities. As I recommended and still do, take a look into CBT and Mindfulness as escapes from the rigors of day-to-day life. Don't forget the stigma around autistic children, and make an effort to spread awareness in your own way, no matter how small. Remember you are not alone and know that you can take solace in the words of other parents from the raisingchildren.net.au video in chapter seven.

There is a lot to learn from my realizations while watching American Tragedy, but as I said, it reinforced what I already knew. The major takeaway is that the most effective approaches for social and emotional learning should be integrated into school curriculums and provide skill building across all grade levels to reach all children. This lends itself to the best social and emotional learning efforts as proactive, not reactive.

On the topic of proactivity, another point to consider is the transition from childhood through puberty, which is tough for any child. However, autistic children may have big struggles coping with the biological changes. Neurodivergent girls have been noted to have trouble interacting socially with neurotypical girls during puberty, with adverse effects on mental health. This is not to say that boys find it any easier, but the proactive endeavors to brace children for puberty will only do them favors. You want your child to gain some form of independence, which is facilitated by teaching social skills, including masking, and why it should be avoided.

It is a good idea to anticipate changes and develop support systems, in addition to showing your child that neurodivergence means many strengths through the teenage years and into adulthood, which is a great self-esteem booster. Educating children on unhealthy relationships with social media, as well as the good that can come of social media, in preparation for when your child takes an interest, can prevent cyberbullying and the other evils of the internet. The three YouTube channels that I listed at the end of chapter 8 are worth looking at. Firstly, as a parent, and then with your child as a parent/ teacher.

I am confident that you'll be able to give your children the words, but if not, you will be able to give them the feelings and the means to self-expression. So, although words are important, the overriding importance is communication. On that note, I would like to leave you with a quote from author Peter Drucker:

The most important part about communication is to hear what is not being said.

Sometimes, we need to hear what our children are not saying so that we can give them the words!

The Pivot for Parents and Educators: ADHD/Autism

How Looking Through a Different Lens at the
Neurodivergent Mind Can Change Our Thoughts and
Feelings About a Diagnosis

Kim Gallo, M.S. CCC-SLP

Introduction

In the late 90s, I answered an advertisement on a college bulletin board. It was for a position as a tutor or trainer for a toddler diagnosed with autism. It said, "No experience is necessary. Will train!"

I interviewed, and I went on to be "hired" by that family for that position. I was trained by a Behavior Analyst to provide Applied Behavior Analysis therapy or, as it was called at the time, discrete trial therapy. Through that family, I met several other families looking for help with their ABA-home program. These opportunities changed the trajectory of my life. I went on to earn a bachelor's degree in psychology and later became a Board-Certified Associate Behavior Analyst. Many families I worked with at the time worked with the same Speech-Language Pathologist, Donna W. On many occasions, I had the opportunity to accompany these students to speech therapy. Meeting Donna W. each week and watching her in therapy working with kids has also changed my life.

A few years later, I enrolled in graduate school to become a Speech-Language Pathologist. I was lucky enough to complete my internship alongside my mentor, Donna W. Much of her private practice was dedicated to helping families with autistic kids learn how to communicate and develop social skills. Around the same time, I gave birth to my first child, my daughter Kayle. Kayle appeared to be "typically developing" in her early years. She was bright, chatty, theatrical, and resilient. She was also disorganized and short-tempered, and she struggled to follow directions more and more as she grew.

In October, when she was eight years old and in the third grade, we decided to take a family trip to the local pumpkin patch. It was a day I'll never forget. It should have been a fun yet ordinary day. But we all left feeling upset, and at the time, Kayle, her brother, and I all cried at some point on this day. What happened? Nothing really, but everything was a challenge for Kayle. She just never seemed to listen, from getting out of the car to asking her to hold my hand or stay near me, to not touch everything, to leave her brother alone, to ask her to try to be quiet when adults were talking. Next thing you know, my husband is cranky, my three-year-old son is fussy, and I am over-the-top frustrated, trying my hardest to satisfy everyone while keeping the kids safe. So, what should have been a pleasant fall outing for a family of four turned into complete misery.

Upon arriving home that day, I remember crying in the bathroom, wondering where I was going wrong. I had a smart, healthy, "normal" kid. Why was she so defiant? So strong-willed? Remember, I was a Behaviorist and a Speech-Language Pathologist. Why were none of the tools in my toolbox working here? I tried positive and negative reinforcement. I tried token economies. I tried positive and negative punishment, small rewards, big rewards, anything and everything. Nothing worked. I was starting to feel like Kayle was doing this to me on purpose—something spiteful—but I knew in my heart that that didn't make sense.

I called my old friend Donna W. on that day from the floor of my bathroom. I just wanted to be consoled, but what I got was so much more. Donna suggested that what I was describing did not sound like it was in Kayle's control. I was shocked and a little relieved at the idea that this thing going on with Kayle could potentially not be anyone's fault or in anyone's control. Soon after that conversation, I brought her in for some psycho-educational testing, and she received the diagnosis of ADHD. Today, Kayle is a young woman. She earned a college degree at that same school where I saw that advertisement on the bulletin board in the late 90s.

She has a job, she has friends, and she is an athlete who swam on a nationally-ranked Synchronized Swim team for over a decade. While she still has challenges and struggles related to her diagnosis, finding out about that diagnosis, as well as my mindset regarding that diagnosis, has changed our lives. Reflecting on that day, I realize how grateful I am for my friendship with Donna and for Kayle's diagnosis. It allowed me to feel differently about Kayle. I was angry and frustrated much of the time when we were together back then. Knowing that she is neurodivergent allows me to pivot my perspective about what I expect, how I think, what I think, and how I teach and parent. This experience, along with over 20 years of working with neurodivergent individuals, has led me to want to share some of my knowledge and information with you. I know our children are likely quite different, but I hope that after reading this book, you will have a pivot of your own.

This book is designed to spread awareness and help the

autistic community find a platform for change. Traditional approaches to autism need to be changed, and as a parent, it is my responsibility to do that. Autistic children, and to a lesser degree, ADHD children, experience the world in a different manner, and our focus needs to be on a difference, not a disability, abnormality, or special needs.

You may have heard the terms "neurotypical" and "neurodiverse," which I explain in detail. The idea is that autistic children have neurodiverse minds, with a focus on the diverse part. Neurotypical refers, for these purposes, to non-autistic individuals who experience life in a different manner than their neurodiverse counterparts. I set out the differences in terms of cognitive and brain function, in addition to the ways in which neurotypical people are different from each other.

I place focus on the type of language that should be used in the pursuit of affirming language that promotes inclusion as opposed to isolation. Words are powerful and have the ability to cause emotional distress. We do not want that.

Studies suggest that telling children that they are autistic at a younger age allows for a better quality of life as they grow older. (Cage, E. et al, 2017.). That aspect is explored from a results-based point of view and also from a human point of view. Interestingly, the identification of autistic boys is easier than the identification of autistic girls, which I explain in conjunction with the unique world experience that autistic individuals have.

I place focus on a woman by the name of Eustacia Cutler,

who faced difficulties raising an autistic child in the 1950s. As one can imagine, the stigma in those days was huge, but Cutler refused to accept it and brought up her daughter in a household that promoted the celebration of difference. I also explain how Cutler's daughter, Dr. Temple Grandin, handled herself through life as an autistic person.

The sensory experience for autistic children is particularly difficult, and contrary to popular belief, we have eight senses. I laid out what those senses are and how they impact the quality of life of autistic children. One has to remember that dealing with sensory overload is a big challenge, and I pay attention to the different sensory-stimulating behaviors that contribute to coping mechanisms. Expanding on this concept, there is a section on management via self-regulatory behavior and how parents and educators can assist in the development of these behaviors in a positive manner. I then move on to address emotional and cognitive control as well as visual, auditory, and olfactory regulation. Sensory integration therapy is the next theme, with examples of exercises that parents and educators can implement.

Empathy can be a problematic skill for autistic individuals, and Dr. Damian Milton's "double empathy" theory, which I explore, details the hurdles in understanding the experiences of others in an empathetic way. Another point of focus on the social development of autistic children is Michelle Garcia Winner's company, Social Thinking ©. Garcia has been instrumental in explaining how we make sense of life through what is called our meaning maker, which provides us with context.

I discuss the social challenges that autistic children have, from adapting to varying social situations to understanding sarcasm, displaying manners, and engaging in back-and-forth conversation as well as initiating conversation. I explain how parents can prepare their autistic children for these situations via exercises that allow the identification of social cues. Communication forms a large part of this section, specifically communication in friendships. The four levels of friendship—acquaintance, casual, close, and intimate—are dealt with in a way that shows parents and educators how to give autistic children a more meaningful sense of relationships.

The next section handles sports and how autistic children can benefit from social interactions through sports. Furthermore, the preference is individual sports, but with others, such as horseback riding or martial arts.

The three "R's" of bullying are brought into focus, i.e., recognize, respond, and report, before a short section that re-emphasizes empathy.

Constructive language follows, along with the importance of describing things in a way that is conducive to inclusion. I do use "high-functioning" and "low-functioning," although that is not ideal. However, they form the basis of human application, not just autistic function. As part of this section, routines, specific interests, food preferences, social anxiety, and overwhelm are dealt with in detail, followed by an analysis of the three levels of autism and the corresponding levels of support each one requires.

The focus turns to highlighting information regarding different programs at schools that allow the integration of autistic children with neurotypicals. Specifically, IEPs, give parents the opportunity to work in conjunction with educators and therapists, to develop programs suitable to the support needs of their autistic children.

Sadly, autistic individuals do not have a long-life span, on average. The reason for self-harm is that depression and other mental health problems are known to accompany autism. I also note the difficulties with healthcare, including affordability, then bring attention to the appropriateness of the infinity symbolism of autism as opposed to the puzzle piece. This section concludes with explanations as to how autism is not just a neurotype, including some information on the nuts and bolts of "neuro" and what the ramifications of late identification of autism are.

I move forward to assess what emotions are evoked when your child is identified as autistic. It can be a tough time, and feelings of anger or regret about parenting techniques are common. On the other hand, relief is also felt quite regularly, and there is a grief cycle specific to what happens after finding out that your child is autistic. The cycle is explored and explained prior to acceptance.

Two pieces of writing, Welcome to Holland, and Welcome to Beirut, form part of my analysis. The former looks at what it is like to find out that your child has down syndrome and how it affects parenting thereafter. The latter is somewhat of a parody of the former but explains the same subject after receiving news that your child is autistic.

Parenting is stressful, as we all know, and as parents, we need to take time for ourselves. This particular section is about maintaining the correct mindset, taking life day by day with a bit of forward planning, but also being kind to yourself as a parent. I delve into mindfulness techniques, which promote presence and focus on the now. These techniques can be implemented by the parents and introduced to their children in efforts to improve the quality of life for both.

The last section looks at hope for the future, and the fact that autistic individuals have unique personalities, even though challenges are abundant. The "Big Five" personality model is explored, as well as the positive and negative manifestations thereof. Finally, I set out the theory of mind, and its categorization of deficit, before signing off with a challenge to prove the theory wrong, as your child grows into a person of value, through the ability to give and receive love.

Chapter 1

How the Neurodivergent Mind Works

Neurodiversity is a term that many people, even parents of autistic children, may not be aware of. As the name suggests, the concept is based on the premise that our minds are diverse to the point where we experience the world in vastly different ways. Our brains are so intricate that it is not possible for us all to see the world in the same way. There is no right way of experiencing life, meaning that thoughts and behaviors that would have previously been classified as "deficits" should be reclassified simply as differences.

Different Types of Neurodivergence

This book is specifically focused on neurodivergence in autism and Attention Deficit Hyperactivity Disorder (ADHD). However, I will list the other types of neurodiversity for the sake of completeness before directing focus to autism and ADHD:

- Tourette's Syndrome

- Dyslexia

- Dyspraxia

- Dyscalculia

- Dysgraphia

- Meares-Irlen Syndrome

- Hyperlexia

- Synaesthesia

- Aspergers

- Pathological Demand Avoidance

- Sensory Processing Disorder

Neurodivergence can also be said to encompass mental illnesses such as schizophrenia and bipolar disorder, but the jury is still out on the accuracy of this idea. Interestingly, neurodivergence goes beyond differences in function, depending on the type of neurodivergence at its core. Gender, race, and culture also play a significant role, which makes logical sense considering that those three categories experience life differently as it is.

What Makes Neurodivergent Brains Different?

The best way of addressing the differences in a neurodivergent brain is by drawing comparisons with a neurotypical brain. The former, as explained above, manifests in various conditions, but an all-encompassing conclusion is that neurodivergent brains experience difficulties with soft skills. This is a term that is often used in relation to employment but fundamentally applies to social interactions in general. An example is speaking too loudly or standing uncomfortably close to someone in public. In times of stress, neurodivergent individuals may rock back and forth as a self-soothing exercise, which is also a hallmark of struggles with soft skills.

Further differences include irregularity of mood and an unconscious reluctance to pay attention to stimuli. Neurodivergent individuals may vary in behavior, often when approaching learning or sociability. The idea that these manifestations are different, not abnormal, largely rejects the medical model of disability, which is discussed in further detail later in this book.

The neurotypical brain is commonly acknowledged as one that displays typical cognitive ability and intellectual application. Individuals falling into this category meet traditionally accepted developmental milestones within a relatively standardized time period. Other accepted characteristics of neurotypical behavior include the ability to recognize when one is standing too close to another or speaking too loudly, given the social setting. The observable presumption is that communication skills and developing social connections without being overcome by noise or light, for example, are relatively easy for neurotypical brains.

As parents, friends, employers, or colleagues of Autistic or ADHD children and young adults, it is important to understand that the terms neurodivergent and neurotypical go a long way toward encompassing differences and putting aside the idea of abnormality. The use of language is perhaps more important than one may think.

Affirming Language

Take a simple exercise that is done day in and day out by parents and educators around the world when teaching language to young children. A picture of a cat is shown to the child, with the word "cat" written below. With repetition, the child learns to associate what they see with the word that is used to describe it. The repetition part is the affirmation that the picture and the word are linked.

Parents who call their children stupid are affirming stupidity, even though that may not be the case. If someone hears something over and over again, they will start to believe it. For these reasons, it is necessary to change the way that we use language in the realm of autism and ADHD. Remember, differences are not deficiencies!

Emma Ward, artist, autism advocate, and mother of four, encapsulated the concept brilliantly, and I quote: "The way we talk to our children is how they will talk about themselves. I choose to surround my family with voices that raise us up" (Ward, E, n.d.).

As a start, let's look at autism, fully described as Autistic Spectrum Disorder. The term "disorder" is problematic. When we think of a disorder, the conclusion is that something is wrong or has gone wrong. However, relabeling autism in its full form as Autistic Spectrum Difference, removes the misapprehension that something is wrong and replaces it with the notion that something is different.

The same thinking applies to the following:

- Sensory Processing Difference, not Sensory Processing Disorder.

- My child is autistic, not my child has autism.

- Identified as autistic, not diagnosed with autism.

- Inclusive education, not special education.

- Passions or hobbies, not restricted interests, or obsessions.

These subtle differences in semantics can have a significant impact on how a child views themselves as a person. In a child's formative years, parental influence is what shapes the child, which is why parents need to use affirming language to validate and celebrate their autistic identity. The same must apply to educators. Teachers and therapists are next in line as influential figures in the young lives of children. Parents give up a lot of power and influence when they drop their kids off at school or at therapy, which is why educators need to practice inclusivity. It is likely that an autistic or ADHD child has heard words such as "disorder," "treatment," "symptoms," or "abnormal" from doctors and other medical people. This type of language affirms abnormality, and it is the job of educators and parents to dispel those words with inclusive affirmations centered around difference. Admittedly, medical professionals should also be using the correct affirmations. However, when parents with autistic or ADHD children start seeing doctors for the first time, they have no idea what harm the traditionally used language can cause.

The ramifications of using the "old language" can place limitations on autistic or ADHD children. Self-esteem issues, insecurities, an altered sense of identity, and acceptance of "being broken" can stay with a child into adulthood. The terms "high-functioning" and "low-functioning" are particularly damaging and can also be frustrating when heard by parents. On one hand, the use of the term's reeks of ignorance, and on the other, people use them innocently. No matter who you are, your functional abilities differ on a daily basis. Late nights make one tired and affect work performance, as well as general day-to-day activities. So why do we label differences in autistic and ADHD children in such a way as to affirm that there is something wrong? The correct terms are "specific strengths" and "needs," which terms apply to every human alive.

Autistic children need therapy, educational strategies, and love, not treatments or interventions. They do not have special needs; they do have individual needs. Autistic children are non-speaking, not nonverbal. They have an intricate language without the need to speak. Autistic children do not have anything wrong with them. They are different, as are we all, and as parents and educators, we need to affirm that.

Does Teaching a Child That They Are Autistic at a Younger Age Create Better Adult Outcomes?

Several studies have been conducted on this subject. The most relevant study is a very recent one, which I will summarize. The full citation is contained in the references section, as the study was conducted by several academics (Oredipe et al., 2022). No similar study has ever been done, and the only available research suggests that support given to autistic children in the past did lead to better adult outcomes. Past studies may have glossed over the concept of telling children at young ages that they are autistic, or perhaps such a concept was just not part of the study. Either way, the 2022 study indicates progress and is a very welcome one.

Seventy-eight university students participated and were asked three questions, as follows:

- How did you learn that you were autistic?

- How did you feel about autism when you first learned that you were autistic?

- When would you tell autistic children about their autism?

The fundamental findings were:

- A higher quality of life and well-being as adults were present in the students who were told that they were autistic when they were young children.

- Learning at an older age that one is autistic showed associations with more positive emotions and also a higher quality of life.

The above two conclusions may be easily conflated, but the major difference is quality of life as opposed to feelings about one's autism. However, the common denominator was being told at a young age.

The follow-on findings were:

- The students who were told that they were autistic in later life did display positive emotions towards autism.

- A possible reason is the sense of relief that was felt in discovering that there was an explanation for their differences.

- The study suggested that the students who learned that they were autistic later in life may be better placed to interact with autistic communities and become involved in the neurodivergent movement.

Shared experiences are a tool that brings people together, and it was found that some children and young teenagers first felt negative emotions after being told that they were autistic. Positivity grew with age and the discovery of other autistic individuals with whom they could talk about past experiences.

Not one of the students said that they would wait until adulthood. In fact, some were of the opinion that they would tell their children as soon as they became old enough to understand. One particular student articulated the way that they would tell their child very well, and to quote directly: "I would tell my child that autism is a different way of thinking, that it can be challenging and beautiful and powerful and exhausting and impactful, that autistic people deserve to be themselves, to be proud of their identity, and to have supports that help them meet their needs."The study clearly shows that a child who learns they are autistic at a younger age is better prepared for greater well-being and quality of life. Furthermore, being told at a younger age allows for learning from life experiences, making it easier to attain said well-being and quality of life. The resounding outcome is that it is most definitely the case that teaching a child that they are autistic at a younger age creates better adult outcomes.

How Do Gender Differences Impact Children With Neurodivergent Minds?

Research shows that autistic boys and girls may experience autism in different ways. Girls tend to be identified as autistic later than boys, but interestingly, autistic boys outnumber girls significantly. This has been attributed to the biological differences between the sexes. However, the manner in which neurodivergence manifests in autistic boys and girls may explain the different impact on young neurodivergent minds.

According to research, for every autistic girl, there are four autistic boys (de Giambattista et al., 2021). Signs or traits of autism differ only slightly between boys and girls and can therefore be easily missed, leading to a misinterpretation of support needs in girls. It has been suggested that one of the reasons is that girls tend to camouflage or mask. These terms are addressed in Chapter 3, but in summary, they refer to hiding differences, which they perceive to indicate an abnormality.

Unique Interpretation of the World

We have all experienced some form of social anxiety, be it discomfort in large crowds or even being nervous about a job interview. With autistic children, social and other anxieties are amplified, which means that they see and experience the world uniquely. It can be a confusing experience, often characterized by sensory overload. It is as if too much information is whirling around in the brain, leading to displays of differences such as tantrums and social withdrawal. I must reiterate that such displays are merely different coping mechanisms.

In a visual sense, autistic children, in some cases, have a higher awareness of peripheral vision. As one can imagine, this creates a situation where the perception of the environment is more intense. It is almost as if too much is happening at once, which leads to an uncomfortable placement, a looping-over effect, and confusion as to the experience of time and space.

The Stigma

Autism is not a mental illness, although autistic individuals do have a propensity for mental illness. This means that autism is subject to a double stigma: The mental health stigma and the incorrect perception that autism is a disease or sickness. It can be infuriating to consider that people think that depression is a case of "just cheer up" or that autism is a "problem on the fringe of society." For these reasons, more education is required on these topics to dispel ignorance and empower those who are subject to the stigma.

To really address the stigma described above, it is useful to define what a stigma is. The Encyclopedia Britannica's definition is as follows:

"A set of negative and often unfair beliefs that a society or group of people have about something."

Every stigma is slightly different, but there are shared elements. The autism stigma could be said to be unique in that it garners rejection, which is not necessarily the case with stigmas about being poor, homosexual, or mentally ill, for example. Individuals may be weary, frightened, or uncomfortable when they observe different reactions to sensory stimuli by autistic children or adults, for that matter. An ill-timed laugh, a panic attack, or a tantrum might violate the "rules of society," for lack of a better term, and non-autistic people could very well become judgmental.

I don't like the term "violation," as it leans towards the negative. However, it is the correct description in this case. What I mean is the violation of personal space. Autism is synonymous with a lack of spatial awareness, and violating someone else's space is a common occurrence. If an autistic child is standing at a distance considered too close to another child or adult, the other person may not even realize that the child is autistic. The discomfort of the individual may lead to irritation and lashing out, which could cause a reaction that reveals the child's autism and casts judgment upon that child. The reaction feeds the child's thoughts of rejection and perpetuates the "there is something wrong with me" mindset in the child.

One may argue that children lack the cognition to understand the damage that they can do to other children through exclusion and bullying. Unfortunately, autistic children are often not included in activities with peers and are subjected to being picked on. This is not necessarily stigma-related, as it can be further argued that children are excluded based on overt differences, like being overweight. Perhaps one could call it an unconscious propagation of the stigma.

Parents and siblings of autistic or ADHD children are also affected by the stigma. Parenting requires social interactions at events like school plays or children's birthday parties, which are occasions that could trigger anxiety in autistic children, causing socially frowned-upon actions. Parents of other children might avoid parents with autistic children, stop inviting them to gatherings, and avoid them at extracurricular activities. The difficulty is that children ask questions. It is difficult to explain to a child the reasons for not being accepted into social environments anymore. Parents can also feel judged and labeled as bad parents, which is just not fair.

How Exactly Do We Break the Stigma?

To break the stigma, we need to raise awareness and get people talking about autism and ADHD. These things tend to happen slowly, but we have to start somewhere. Social media allows an unprecedented reach that can help to inform and educate. Perhaps high schools can adopt programs that explain autism and affirm that behavior is different, not wrong, or abnormal. There is a day dedicated to autism awareness (April 2), but we need more than that.

Mainstream media is a means that has been used to spread knowledge and understanding on many taboo subjects, as well as dispel stigmas and misapprehensions that people have. There is a Netflix series called Atypical, which I strongly recommend as an educational tool for autism. The main protagonist is an eighteen-year-old autistic boy who is negotiating his way through his teenage life. His behaviors and depiction of what autism is like are very accurate. The show addresses the way in which the world is viewed by the character and the challenges he faces. It also focuses on his family support system and points out the prejudices that are present in real life. The series, which debuted in August 2017, is perhaps a starting point for people interested in learning more about autism and understanding the stigma. If one can understand the stigma, one can start to break it.

Eustacia Cutler and the Autism Stigma

Eustacia Cutler is known worldwide amongst the autism community and has done groundbreaking work on spreading information about autism. Cutler is a former singer and actor, now a speaker and author, and the mother of an autistic daughter. Dr. Temple Grandin. Cutler's association with autism began back in 1950, when her daughter was identified as autistic. During that time in history, there were tremendously powerful stigmas attached to homosexuality, feminism, and racial oppression, so autism stood no chance.

In 1950, autism was seen as a "developmental disability," and many autistic children were institutionalized in stark, gray-stone buildings with poor care, left to feel isolated and alone. Cutler would not have it, and despite her husband's being in favor of putting their daughter in an institution, Cutler refused and decided that Temple would be raised at home.

Cutler struggled to find schools that would accept Temple and heard things such as, "She is a menace to society," "She is retarded," and "She does not belong at a 'normal'" school (Laird, n.d.). New therapies were hard to come by, and Cutler had scant support from her then-husband, but she persisted with what she felt was the best way to raise an autistic child. With age, Temple excelled in academia, and as of 2022, she is an animal behaviorist at Colorado State University. Temple is an advocate for the humane treatment of animals and a beacon of light for autistic children. We all need role models, and teaching children about people such as Cutler and her very successful autistic daughter is a way of providing role models in autism.

I came across an online article by a woman named Chloe Fay, which I have referenced at the end of this book. Fay has a BA in Special Education, and while I do not like the term "special," the nine points listed are very applicable to changing the way we see autism.

Furthermore, the article is very helpful in giving parents and educators a push in the right direction toward breaking the stigma:

- Learn about the history of autism.

- Raise awareness with what you wear.

- Check out the work of famous people with autism.

- Find sensory toys and tools that help.

- Support autism-friendly businesses and employees.

- Read books about autism.

- Spread awareness in your community.

- Spread kindness.

- Read, watch, or listen to something created by an autistic person.

Inge-Marie Eigsti, an autism expert and Ph.D. holder from the University of Rochester, is particularly interested in studies probing the effects of the stigma on families. Speaking about how autistic people look and speak like everyone else and the difficulty in understanding or accepting autistic individuals, Eigsti put forward this opinion (2016):

"For many families, that makes the presence of out-of-control behavior or socially unexpected behavior that much more stigmatizing because there is not a clear indicator of why the child is behaving like that. Parents may worry that the behavior is being attributed to bad parenting skills, laziness, a lack of motivation, or other negative qualities in the child or the family."

It is this type of thinking that needs to be dispelled by raising awareness. As I mentioned previously, a stigma is a set of NEGATIVE and UNFAIR beliefs. Autistic individuals must be treated in a positive and fair manner.

Chapter 2

The Eight Senses

Eight Not Five

Most of us have learned that there are five senses: smell, sound, taste, touch, and sight. In reality, there are three more senses: vestibular, interoceptive, and proprioceptive. As we know, autism is synonymous with sensory overload, and dealing with eight enhanced senses provides its challenges. Let's have a look at those senses and some biological explanations.

Smell

The olfactory system in the brain is what controls the processing of smell. Situated in the forward part of the brain, the olfactory bulb is a conduit that links the brain to the nose.

The bulb operates by

- discriminating among odors.

- enhancing the detection of odors.

- filtering out background odors.

- allow modification in the detection of odors.

Autistic children may experience certain smells in an enhanced manner. The result can be an unwillingness to go to a place associated with a particular smell. A gas station is a good example; fuel has a distinctive smell, and autistic individuals could find that smell intense—an assault on the senses, if you like. Even ordinarily pleasant smells, like perfume or scented shampoo, can be overwhelming.

The resultant anxiety can be partially combated by not taking your autistic child anywhere where there is a likelihood of adverse odors. Cleaning products can be particularly overwhelming for kids with smell sensitivity.

When at home, use unscented shampoo and keep the house well-ventilated.

On the other side of the scale, smells like deodorants or perfumes may be pleasant to autistic children, resulting in their seeking out those smells. Unusual social behavior may be a result, in terms of seeking out smells on people in public and moving too close to such people in order to take in the odors.

Enjoyable smells can be emulated by wearing strong

perfume or carrying a scented handkerchief when in public. You could cook strongly scented meals at home, have nice-smelling flowers in the house, or even burn incense.

Always remember that your autistic child experiences differences, not abnormalities, so you need to continuously affirm that with positive language.

Sound

The auditory cortex, primarily located in the brain's left hemisphere, is tasked with processing sound. The system identifies changes in amplitude and frequency as well as computing combinations of frequencies. Research has shown that gifted musicians tend to have a more powerful auditory system, allowing them to pick up intricacies in sound differentiation that others might not be able to.

Studies suggest that autistic children who experience sound at amplified levels find that forty decibels are extremely loud. A conversation at close quarters is about fifty decibels, and a whispered conversation is around thirty decibels. Considering those statistics, then placing an autistic child in an environment such as a classroom, where conversations, shuffling papers, coughing, and the voice of the teacher are bombarding that child's ears, a severe amount of anxiety is inevitable.

Some therapists discourage the use of noise-canceling headphones. However, they really are a great tool for maintaining calm. Allowing allocated quiet time at home has also proved effective, as have distractions such as playing a game on a phone or iPad. It is all about making an environment as comfortable and non-distracting as possible as a tool to manage anxiety.

Taste

Taste is experienced via the gustatory system. The most commonly used example is the detection of salt. In a primal sense, humans require water, and salt makes us thirsty. The gustatory cortex tells us to add salt to our french fries, which enhances the taste but also creates the need to drink water. Communication is between the brain and the tongue, meaning that we have the ability to understand that biting into a lemon is sour and unpleasant while biting into a bar of chocolate is sweet and pleasurable.

Sensitivity to taste is complicated to solve, but taking your child to a nutritionist can help. You need to figure out which foods provide a horrible eating experience and which foods are nice to eat. It is not uncommon for autistic children to only enjoy a few food types. There is nothing wrong with that, and the way to cater to taste differences is to cook what your child likes and make sure he or she always has a packed snack when not at home. It is not ideal, but it is not the worst thing in the world. Perhaps try to get some of the healthy foods into the pancake batter and mix them thoroughly, in which case your child may not notice. Having said that, malnutrition or vitamin and mineral deficits can creep in, which is another reason talking to a nutritionist might be a good idea.

Food textures, not taste, are often the problem. Many children prefer crunchy foods over soft and mushy foods.

Neurodivergent children are aware when subtle changes are made to their food, which is why "hiding" the healthy foods in soups and batters can sometimes backfire. This, in turn, could potentially cause a child to reject foods they previously consumed. If they have a limited food repertoire to begin with, this can easily turn problematic.

Touch

Identification through touch is regulated by the somatosensory cortex. It is a complex system that also controls the sensations of pressure, temperature, and pain. These sensory feelings are not all strictly touch-related, but the diversity of brain function in this specific area encapsulates them as the primary components of touch.

The term "touchy-feely" comes to mind. Some people prefer a hug, others a handshake or a high five. Autistic children sometimes prefer no form of touch at all. Managing that at home can be very challenging, although emotions regarding a lack of affection may arise in parents or siblings. We still need to encourage acceptance of the differences, even though it is extremely tough. Fear of light touch is incredibly difficult to manage because touch is unavoidable. However, educators and parents can slowly introduce touch for brief periods in order to create acclimatization to touch, leading to less anxiety (Cekaite, 2016). Remember to use a firm touch instead of a light touch. A light touch is arousing to the sympathetic nervous system and can cause a fight-or-flight reaction. Firm touch can inhibit or dampen down the arousal that light touch causes and make touch more tolerable.

Sight

Sight manifests as visual pathways, i.e., neuroscientists distinguish between two visual systems. The "what" system is located at the junction of the occipital lobe and the temporal lobe and is involved in object recognition. The "where" system is located on the junction of the occipital and parietal lobes and is involved in location information (Goldberg, 2022).

The occipital lobe has connections with the parietal and temporal lobes, and this is how visual information is interpreted, resulting in the development of visual perceptual skills. Many autistic individuals have significant strengths in visual perception skills. They will gravitate, at an early age, toward the letters of the alphabet, colors, numbers, geometric shapes, and other types of puzzles.

Visual stimulatory behavior will often involve holding an object very close to one's face, then moving it quickly past one's face. Autistic children are often also fascinated by a rolling or spinning object. Autistic children are often sensitive to the flickering light (as well as to the buzzing sound) of fluorescent lighting. Fabric filters can be hung under fluorescent ceiling lights to dim the effect, or incandescent lighting can be used instead.

Autistic children can be extremely sensitive to light and very specific about colors. Dimmer switches are a good tool to regulate light at home, and sunglasses help in outdoor settings. Preference to one color can be changed by slowly introducing different colored toys or clothing, not that there is anything wrong with a propensity to only one or two colors.

Proprioception

Internal body mapping results from the nervous system's proprioceptive input when infants engage in random movements of their arms and legs. This forms the basis for all motor planning skills, from something as simple as reaching for a ball to something as complex as learning to tie your shoes as a five-year-old. Often, kids with ASD have poor proprioceptive processing, which results in poor motor planning skills, which may result in difficulty with gross or fine motor skills, including oral motor speech and sound production.

Proprioceptive input can regulate and calm the nervous system. I had a student many years ago who was around age three. We often found him laying between the mattress and the box spring of his bed because he liked the feeling of the weight on his body. He instinctively provided himself with proprioceptive input (needed to regulate his nervous system). Today, you can buy a weighted blanket at a store or order a weighted vest online.

Graded muscle control is a function of proprioceptive input. How do you know how hard to push on your pencil without breaking the tip? Those with poor proprioceptive processing will likely use excessive force and fail to understand how to grade their movement. How can you pick up a Styrofoam cup without crushing it if you have poor muscle control? You can't.

There are various fun activities that can be done at home to teach your child how to use physical prowess in order to reduce the intensity of interactions. An obstacle course using different items and requiring lifting, jumping, and turning is a very useful tool. Throwing a ball back and forth, then moving further away, can assist in creating awareness of the speed with which the ball is thrown in relation to distance. You can give your child body massages using varying levels of pressure to illustrate what is too hard and what is too soft. Look at it like preparation for an athletic event by honing the skills needed to participate at intensity levels that are measured and appropriate in social situations.

Vestibular

Balance and motion activation are controlled by the vestibular system, found in the middle ear. Spatial awareness is also controlled by the vestibular system and is something that autistic children struggle to discern. Sports and outdoor activities can help in developing better balance, which also has a positive effect on spatial awareness. Skateboarding, gymnastics, or even skipping will improve balance and give a better understanding of motion. Musical chairs work, as well as dancing, so be creative and cater to your child's different requirements.

Interoception

Interoception is the manner in which communication with internal organs manifests. Autistic children can face situations where feelings of hunger, thirst, warmth, or cold cannot be identified. Teaching children about their bodies by using charts or explaining the cues from our bodies—telling us that we are hungry, tired, or cold—can go a long way toward creating specific awareness. Being unable to identify these body cues can certainly be changed by asking your child whether he or she is hungry or thirsty. Slowly, they will learn that after an exercise, it is likely that they are hungry or that going outside in the winter will make them cold.

Sensory Diet

Taking note of how autistic children process sensory information and then adapt to their environments, as discussed above, can be called "sensory management." It certainly isn't an easy task, but seeing your child's quality of life improves as you implement activities and take measures to cater to their specific needs will be rewarding beyond comprehension. It is typically the role of the Occupational Therapist to assess how an individual processes sensory input and to subsequently develop a "sensory diet" or a specific program of sensory activities that help improve sensory processing and self-regulation.

Self-Regulation

We should all work at self-regulation, and as the name suggests, the practice is one of management in day-to-day life. It requires personal awareness and greater control over how we conduct ourselves. Dr. Temple Grandin, who was mentioned in the previous chapter, offers her own definition as follows:

"The skill of managing feelings so that they don't reach overwhelming levels and interfere with learning and development. Many people on the spectrum need support as they struggle to manage their emotions and mitigate their anxiety."

Even as adults, perhaps especially as adults, we experience emotions that are difficult to regulate. Oversensitivity, anger, impatience, or anxiety can prove problematic. Learning self-regulation from a young age is a step in the right direction for developing skills that can be carried into adulthood. It is widely accepted that self-regulation can be broken up into three categories.

Sensory Regulation

Gives autistic children the skills to identify potentially anxiety-inducing sensory experiences and to respond in a way that mitigates the potential anxiety.

Emotional Regulation

As an aside, it is a pity that social conventions impose rules upon us, restricting the things that we would like to say. We experience a semi-forced suppression of opinions because of politeness, and in autistic children, teaching "socially acceptable" moderation of reactions is the name of the game.

Cognitive Regulation

This involves the shaping of thinking processes for the purposes of greater focus on learning, problem-solving, and persistence.

Implementation

The Zones of Regulation (Kuypers, L.) is a book that sets out a curriculum developed by Leah Kuypers, MA Ed. The curriculum has been adopted by educators and parents around the world and is considered the foremost approach to self-regulation in autistic children. Kuypers is an expert in the field of autism and has worked as an occupational therapist at various public schools in the United States.

Helping Your Children With Self-Regulation

As you may remember, in chapter one, I referred to studies about children benefiting from being told at a young age that they are autistic. One of the students in the study described autism as "challenging and beautiful, powerful, exhausting, and impactful." Such is the journey that educators, and more importantly, parents, walk with autistic children; self-regulation is an important part of that journey.

Stimulatory Behavior

Stimulatory behavior, known as "stimming" or "self-stimming," is often observed in individuals with autism. The practices of rocking back and forth, walking up and down, tapping a pen incessantly, or flicking an elastic band are examples of stimulating behavior that acts as a comfort in overwhelming or anxiety-inducing situations. There is nothing wrong with stimming, and we often do it without even noticing, but it can become disruptive and get in the way of learning. A balance needs to be reached, and the idea is to reduce, change, or introduce replacement stimming exercises that may cause an autistic child to be singled out and isolated. It is simple and complicated at the same time. Let's take the pen-tapping example in a classroom. A good replacement behavior is a foot-tapping at a measured rhythm while reciting "one, two, three, four." If a child can engage in the latter and still draw out the comfort required, then the distraction is almost entirely removed. Parents need to practice with their autistic children at home and slowly introduce behavior notifications or changes.

Any routine is difficult to break or alter, which is why constant work is required, especially considering that stimming will always be present in some form. To use another example, autistic children may struggle to contain the excitement, so jumping up and down, with hand clapping and shrieks, is not unusual. The unfortunate part is that in public places, people stare, and that can negatively affect the child and the child's family. In this instance, the idea is to regulate the behavior so as to create a culture of a shorter, less intense display of excitement. Working on regulating self-stimulatory behavior has shown to have positive effects on the alienation that autistic children can feel as a result of unwanted negative attention during periods of self-stimulatory behavior.

I want to add something about the fact that because we do not want to encourage the masking of self-stimulatory behavior, we need to consider some things, including our individual perspectives on the issue.

Educators of all kinds should be teaching their neurotypical students about why their autistic peers need to self-stimulate. It's to regulate their nervous systems. Yes, it's a difficult concept to understand, but if it is phrased correctly, it can make sense to even the youngest student.

Schools in every state should acknowledge the need for Occupational Therapy services that will address ways to help kids regulate their nervous systems, so the need to self-stim is reduced in the classroom. Sensory integration services are most certainly educationally relevant.

Visual, Auditory, and Olfactory Stimming

Visual

Like other stimming activities, repetition is often a convention of visual stimming. Flicking a light switch on and off, following moving objects with one's eyes, or staring at the television are regular occurrences. Sensory lighting is a good way of creating self-regulation and reducing stress.

Auditory

Again, repetition is evident in auditory stimming and may involve playing a song over and over or making indistinguishable noises for extended periods. An effective method of self-regulation in these instances is maybe something like a bubble tube, which is literally a tube that makes gentle, enjoyable, calming bubbling sounds.

Olfactory

Biting, sniffing, and touching characterize olfactory stimulation and can result in unpleasant experiences when trying food and drinks that are either very bitter or very sweet. To prevent unpleasant experiences, it is necessary to teach children what is beneficial and what is harmful, so the child is aware of what to smell, eat, or touch. Remember, one of the functions of the senses is to protect us from danger, so if the milk smells sour, most neurotypicals know to avoid it. However, in some instances, this may be more of a scenario where one must learn from the unpleasant experience.

The Sensory Funnel

The sensory funnel, created by Aspergers Experts Co-Founder Danny Raede, is divided into five groups that sit on top of each other, reflected in a hypothetical funnel shape. We address the groups from bottom to top— sensory first, followed by emotion, awareness, social skills, and finally, executive function. Raede's Sensory Funnel was developed as a visual tool to showcase the importance of the order in which we must address the needs of neurodivergent. Raede's theory certainly makes sense. How can you really focus, learn, or understand how to improve your social skills or executive function abilities when you are experiencing the discomfort of your body or brain feeling dysregulated?

Sensory

The eight senses, but more specifically, the feelings precipitated by your body, such as anxiety, can perpetuate through throat constriction, increased heart rate, and nervous energy.

Emotional

This category sits above sensory and is the result of anxiety. One can look at it as the sensory experience triggering an emotional reaction.

Awareness

Emotional overload limits awareness, and the focus is purely on the emotional experience, which limits the ability to take in anything else.

Social

Social skills and reading situations can be difficult for autistic children. However, this is something that can be learned through observation, teaching, and practice. To be more specific, autistic children may not understand nonverbal language, such as body language, or they may struggle with how to interpret things said in a conversation.

Executive Function

This can be looked at as the final goal and can be summed up as the ability to be highly functional in environments that have traditionally been anxiety- or stress-inducing.

The following points provide the definition of the term:

- Adaptable thinking: Adjusting to the situation when need be.

- Planning: Thinking about the future, prioritizing, and creating a plan.

- Self-Monitoring: Evaluate how you are doing.

- Self-Control: Maintaining composure despite feelings and emotions.

- Time management: Planning and organizing a schedule to complete a large assignment or time-consuming task.

- Organization: Arranging things in order to maintain some sort of system.

Sensory Integration

Our brains interpret the way in which we react to experiencing feelings and emotions based on our eight senses in different situations. Integration comes in as the function that joins the processing of a combination of different senses. The good news is that scientific analysis has shown that therapeutic assistance has enjoyed success in regulating the unpleasant processing of sensory interpretation. Sensory integration is primarily the interconnection between tactile, proprioceptive, and vestibular functions.

Sensory Integration Therapy (SIT)

SIT is by no means new; it was first explored in the 1970s by an occupational therapist and psychologist A. Jean Ayres. SIT is a therapeutic approach that is used by Occupational Therapists to improve symptoms of sensory integration dysfunction.

One should involve the therapist in guiding the child through the "just right" challenge of navigating sensory activities in order to improve sensory processing and produce an "adaptive response" on the part of the child. Ayres theorized that the behavior and learning problems were, in part, due to faulty integrations of sensory information and the inability of higher centers to modulate and regulate lower brain sensory-motor centers (Ayers, 1972).

Sensory Processing

This was partially dealt with in the prior examination of the eight senses, but for the sake of completeness: The perception of the senses, followed by the manner in which the senses are understood, and the arrangement of the sensory experience make up what is called "sensory processing."

What Is the Difference Between Sensory Integration and Sensory Processing?

The terms are used interchangeably, and it may be argued that the differences are subtle, if not absent. The bottom line is that both terms refer to the brain receiving information and instructing the body to act in accordance with that information.

Sensory Modulation Difficulties

It can be challenging to gauge the intensity required in reactions to sensory input, which often gives the impression of a misbehaving child or a bad parent. Being over-responsive to sensory input is just as normal as being under-responsive. The latter conjures ideas that a child is disinterested, absorbed in themselves, and unwilling to participate, in a classroom setting, for instance. Over-responsiveness is on the other side of the scale and involves extreme excitement, which is characterized by shouting, making noises, fidgeting, and unfortunately, being disruptive during class. It can be exceptionally difficult to tailor or modulate different behaviors, but if successful, it can create a much better quality of life.

Remember, a tantrum from a neurotypical child is completely different from a perceived tantrum from an autistic child. In fact, autistic children are experiencing sensory overload, which looks like a tantrum to an outsider but is not an actual tantrum. Scientifically, the amygdala is triggered. This is the fight-or-flight response area of the brain, which takes effect upon sensory overload.

Sensory Discrimination and Perceptual Problems

Discrimination is the brain's ability to interpret information and disregard its irrelevant parts. In autistic children, the brain can mix up information or organize it in a way that does not correspond with the sensory stimuli. There are a whole host of instances in which this occurs, but below is a list of the more frequently observed manifestations of difficulty with sensory discrimination, as in the inability to:

- Describe or identify objects through touch and/or sight.

- Discern taste differences.

- Judge how loudly or softly to speak.

- Pay attention to others.

- Perceive depth, elevation, or distance.

- Judge how much force to use when picking up an object, throwing a ball, or closing a door.

- Recognize hunger or thirst.

- Identify that they need to use the bathroom.

Vestibular Bilateral Functioning Problems

Autistic children who experience vestibular-bilateral functioning problems lack awareness of their bodies and the space that they are in. The manifestations can be difficulties in maintaining good posture and a neutral head position using the two sides of the body together, as well as disorientation, stumbling, and general clumsiness.

Sympathetic Nervous System

We have all heard of "fight-or-flight," and this categorization is responsible for our defense mechanism when faced with a situation that is terrifying or fear-inducing. Another name is the Mobilization System or the Aggressive Defense System. On one end are anger and rage, while on the other end are fear and panic. When a distress signal is sent from the part of the brain called the amygdala, the hypothalamus activates the sympathetic nervous system by sending signals through the autonomic nerves to the adrenal glands. Epinephrine (adrenaline) and norepinephrine (noradrenaline) are released, which cause an accelerated heart rate, widening of the bronchial passages, and decreased motility (movement) of the large intestine.

Constricted blood vessels cause pupil dilation, activate goose bumps, induce sweating, and raise blood pressure. Some neurodivergent children and adults have an overactive Sympathetic Nervous System because they are stressed by what appears to neurotypicals as everyday things.

Remember, what looks, feels, and smells perfectly fine to a neurotypical might feel tortuous to a neurodivergent, resulting in the neurodivergent's body setting off the fight-or-flight response right there at the breakfast table when trying to gobble down the soggy cereal. We would expect it to go off when we are fighting off a life threat or to flee from an enemy. How sad and uncomfortable for our kiddos to be experiencing this rapid heartbeat and sweating while trying to choke down their cereal.

Sensory Seeking vs. Sensory Avoiding

The concept is simple: Some autistic children enjoy certain sensory experiences and seek them out. Others find similar sensory experiences awful and seek to avoid them. Here are a few examples:

Seeking

- Enjoy different smells

- Prefer being barefoot

- Give bear hugs frequently

- Love being tickled

- Making excessively loud noises

Avoiding

- Does not like being touched

- Finds loud noises unpleasant

- Removes labels from clothes due to the feel on the skin

- Very picky with food

- Turns lights off

Sensory Input

The American Psychological Association (ASA) Dictionary of Psychology defines sensory input as "the stimulation of a sense organ, causing a nerve impulse to travel to its appropriate destination in the brain or spinal cord." To break that down, the response given by a sensory organ when it is stimulated is the actual input. The sensory organs are, of course, the eyes, tongue, skin, ears, and nose.

Sensory Seeking Expanded

Further to the bullet points above, sensory seeking does require more detail, specifically in terms of activities that can create better organizational interactions with the world in general. Deep pressure is encouraged, using a foam roller to activate muscle movement, for instance. Encourage your child to play outside, especially with activities such as climbing trees or riding a bicycle. Use a yoga ball as a seat during homework time, so your child can maintain movement in a positive way. Have pillow fights, play tag, or put music on and dance with your child. Remember that you know your child best, so be creative and tailor activities to his or her needs.

Sensory Avoiding Expanded

The differences between sensory seeking and avoiding are huge, as are the exercises that can help autistic children come to terms with and accept sensory experiences. As awful as it sounds, parents have to test out reactions to stimuli. If your autistic child does not like the feel of clothes, then offer options and note the reactions. Prepare your child for stress-inducing activities to allow mental preparation or anticipation. Cook meals that your child enjoys; get them to help you with the dishes so they can experience soapy water. In contrast to sensory seeking, there is a lot of trial and error, with much more talking and explaining.

Three Pivot Practice Stories

The Sensory Funnel

While meeting with one of my adult autistic students, we began discussing the sensory funnel. He clearly understood my brief explanation and stated it in this manner:

If I go to a venue or even if I am expected to go to a venue where everything is not going to work for me, I become anxious. For example, it depends on "Who" will be there, "Where" it will occur, "What" the activity will be, and

"What" the food will be. If any one of those things is a sensory trigger, I won't want to go! On the other hand, if I am in a one-on-one situation with someone I know and in a familiar venue, I will be happy and calm. Don't try to teach me social skills when I am in an overloaded state!

Sensory Regulation to Avoid Others

One of my students was very gifted and able to attend a school for the arts. He could be picked out of a crowd easily as, in the middle of summer, he would be seen wearing a long-sleeved shirt, a tie, a woolen sport coat, and long pants. I was always curious about this and assumed that he wore it to calm his nervous system. As I got to know him better, I inquired about his garb. He admitted that he dressed this way to keep others from approaching him! And he reported that it was quite effective.

Unique Perspective

Many years ago, while working with a four-year-old child with autism, I attempted to get him to engage with me by both looking and listening. This little guy, while looking away, reported that "it hurts" to do both at the same time and said, "When I try to do both, I can't understand what you are saying!" I thanked him for clearly stating why he refused to engage visually. His sensory systems simply could not work together. The child was the teacher!

Chapter 3

To Mask or Not to Mask

As mentioned earlier, girls seem to be better at masking than young boys. Masking, which is also called camouflaging, is the practice of acting in a way that would be seen as "normal" or "socially acceptable." It is not unique to autism, and if we think about it logically, we all engage in masking on an everyday basis. For example, you have an argument with your partner one morning before leaving for work. On the way, you stop for a coffee, and the server asks you how you are. You smile and tell that person that you are doing well when, in fact, you are upset and irritated by your partner. One could call that a mild form of masking because if every person in that situation answered the polite question, "How are you today?" in the actual way that they felt, nothing would ever get done.

Autistic children can be seen by the world as strange or different, which creates alienation. To avoid feelings of alienation, autistic children will act the way that their non-autistic peers act. Autistic children can suffer from social burnout or exhaustion from continued masking.

The reason is that it takes a fair amount of thought and effort to remember to use the correct hand gestures, facial expressions, reactions, and discussions. The end goal for an autistic child who uses masking is to appear as if they are not different. Being different and experiencing the world differently is okay, normal, and should be socially acceptable. Although masking has been created as a social construct, there should not be a need for it, but it does occur. There are different types of masking, as well as different reasons for engaging in masking.

Types of masking:

- Disguising self-stimulating behavior

- Pre-scripting conversations

- Forcing eye contact

- Giving generic responses to questions

- Hiding personal interests

- Hiding anxiety or stress caused by sensory stimuli

Possible reasons for masking:

- Avoid bullying

- Make friends

- Avoiding the (unnecessary) stigma

- Fitting in

- Doing well in school

As one can imagine, having constant awareness and focusing on not being yourself most of the time is exhausting. A 2019 study published in the Journal of Autism and Developmental Disorders (Cage, E. et al, 2017) concluded that masking certainly has an adverse effect on mental health in autistic individuals. Stress and anxiety levels among participants in the survey were partic

ularly high. Such is completely understandable, given that it is almost impossible to relax while knowing you have to mask the way you really are. Interestingly, it was found that interactions between autistic children and their parents at home showed a release of stress and anxiety. Often, the home environment is one in which autistic children take a reprieve from masking, which brings on the release of built-up stress and anxiety. Exhaustion also sits in this category, and one can imagine closing the front door after a long day of masking, breathing a huge sigh of relief, and collapsing onto one's bed, completely exhausted.

In 2017, Eilidh Cage, also part of the aforementioned 2019 study, along with two fellow researchers, interviewed 111 autistic adults in 2017 and concluded that those who actively engaged in masking had a much higher propensity for depression. Reverting back to childhood, it was proposed that telling children that they are autistic at a younger age is a good tool to alleviate masking, which in turn has positive ramifications for future mental health issues. (Cage, E. et al, V, 2017.).

In terms of suicidal thinking, masking on a continuous basis creates the self-imposed impression that the child is not good enough or is too different from everyone else. An autistic child who grows up believing that difference is a bad thing will focus on their differences in a negative manner. The commonly noted type of suicidal thinking can be described as a spoken sentence: "If I am dead, then I will not have any consciousness, which means that I will not have to hide my true self, which means that my stress, anxiety, depression, and pain will not exist anymore."

Autistic Burnout

Autistic burnout can manifest in several ways, including through neglect in looking after oneself. As parents of autistic children, it is important to ensure that your child is eating well and taking proper care of themselves. Going into adulthood and being unsupervised in times of burnout can result in poor eating, not washing or brushing teeth, not tidying up, and a loss of interest in doing any form of physical activity. Identifying burnout in your child and explaining what it is can go a long way toward reducing its severity as your child gets older and approaches adulthood. Difficulty regulating emotions is also a sign of burnout and is characterized by irritability, lack of patience, an unwillingness to communicate, and withdrawal from familiar activities. At the risk of over-stressing the point, we need to understand and educate autistic children on the results of masking, such as burnout, which predicts a better ability to manage emotions.

Loss of Identity

If a child gets so used to masking in order to create a life consistent with being accepted and included, he or she may start to become the mask and stray away from being the child. This is quite an often-observed phenomenon, not only in autistic children, but it can be excruciatingly difficult to have a sense of not knowing who you are anymore. There are arguments that masking is not necessarily a terrible behavior, but in situations where a child drifts through their younger years feeling lost and disenfranchised, it most certainly is.

Delayed Identification of autism

Simply put, masking is hiding. If a child begins masking from a young age, which is often the case, then parents and educators may have no way of identifying that a child is autistic. As mentioned above, girls tend to favor masking and be better at it than boys, which is why identifying an autistic girl child is more difficult than identifying an autistic boy child. Another difficulty is that, after identifying your child as autistic, the social belief that your child was not autistic but is now suddenly autistic can be harmful to children and parents. One can draw a comparison to depression outside of autism. The stigma makes many depressed individuals hide their depression in social interactions. If the time comes to open up about being depressed, friends and family who have observed the fake-happy persona may label the depressive as a "drama queen" or an "attention seeker." The interesting but also upsetting part is that children are not taught masking but rather start masking on their own.

Camouflaging

The below analysis, cited in the referencing section, was summarized by Rachel Worsley of Reframing Autism, which is a non-profit organization that does incredible work in the field of autistic studies and education. Worsley gives a stripped-down version of an academic investigation in wording that is relatable and understandable to non-academic parents and teachers. The research was conducted in the form of interviews involving seventeen autistic adults. Each participant had filmed conversations with a complete stranger and, at a later stage, had a loosely structured interview while watching the videos of the discussions. The idea was to get an understanding of camouflaging as identified by the "camouflager" so as to guarantee the accuracy of the exercise.

Definition of Camouflage

For the purposes of the study, camouflaging was described as "the dynamic process through which autistic individuals modify their innate autistic social behavior to adapt to, cope within, and/or influence the predominantly neurotypical social environment" (Cook, J. et al, 2022).

The Findings

Thirty-eight different camouflaging behaviors were observed and split into four categories. Considering that there are so many camouflaging behaviors, it is no wonder that exhaustion, stress, and anxiety are possible results of camouflaging.

The four categories are:

- Masking: In this sense, masking was avoided; participants were reluctant to talk about themselves in any personal detail, even when it came to hobbies or general daily activities. Suppression of self-stimming behavior was noticeable, and during the post-stranger discussion interviews, it was apparent that some of the autistic individuals did not disclose their autism.

- Innocuous Engagement: Participants reported deflecting conversation away from themselves by apologizing for social faux pas or making excuses for behavior that was by no means problematic but just different. Other participants played down their intelligence or knowledge of their own areas of interest. There was a general theme of self-taught social conventions: Looking the stranger in the eyes, smiling, and laughing. The category being classified as innocuous is because the conversations lacked depth, not because the autistic individuals were afraid of depth but rather of how they would be perceived.

- Modeling Neurotypical Information: Tactics falling into this subsection included efforts to come across as neurotypical by displaying conventional hand gestures and other body languages, as well as slowing speech and aiming for clarity during discussions.

- Active Self-Preservation: Participants revealed that they created pre-planned topics of conversation that would open up channels of communication. During the discussions, there was a concerted effort to engage in equal amounts of talking and listening.

Importance of the Study

Academic studies should be regular and progressive. This study was the first of its kind, and the knowledge that was obtained is a resource or tool that can be used to assist autistic individuals in shedding the need to mask. The more that is known about a subject, the more that can be done to address the practicalities of the subject.

Self-Stimulating Behavior in Masking and Camouflaging

Clapping one's hands versus flapping with one's hands is an example of how some autistics may mask their natural, innate desire to exhibit self-stimulatory behavior. They are attempting to self-stim less, or in a more acceptable way, to appear more neurotypical. Many autistics may attempt to mask their emotions by not expressing them physically, so they don't jump or pace repeatedly to show their happiness as their bodies are naturally inclined to do. Avoiding self-talk or social situations altogether are other examples of masking self-stimulatory behavior.

What Is Double Empathy?

Dr. Damian Milton's double empathy theory is one that succinctly explains the disparities between autistic and non-autistic people. It also highlights the way in which society displays prejudice, sometimes unknowingly, towards autistic individuals (Milton, D., 2018). Dr. Milton has been recognized for several years through his lecturing career at the University of Kent. He is also an author, the chair of the Participatory Autism Research Collective, and, of course, the force behind the double empathy theory.

The theory puts forward the idea that one group always finds it difficult to put themselves in another group's shoes or attach themselves to another group's experiences by virtue of the fact that such experiences are different. As a result, empathizing with each other is difficult, perhaps impossible. Applied to autism, and as we know, autistic children display and experience emotions differently, as well as communication, relationships, and general world experience. Autistic individuals can lack insight into neurotypical behavior and vice versa, meaning that non-autistic individuals often struggle to empathize with neurodivergent people. It is basically a case of incorrect interpretation or a lack of mutual insight, which creates what is known as "the empathy gap."

Non-autistic communication and empathy tools are typical, whereas the atypical presentation of communication and empathy is different and often labeled as wrong or incorrect. Even though the empathy gap is experienced by neurotypical and neurodivergent groups, there is inequality in terms of the way that empathy is felt in both groups. The assumption is that the non-autistic communication and empathy method represents the correct way to engage. It is obvious that this assumption is prejudicial to autistic people and their communicative and empathetic behaviors. There is thus a misconception that autistic people are just people with broken parts to their disposition or personality.

Due to this misconception, there is a social expectation that autistic people must fix their broken parts so that they can behave and interact like non-autistic people. Unfortunately, traditional therapy, which has become outdated and is frankly archaic, has used the reward system, in which an autistic child is coached into behaving non-autistically in exchange for a reward. The converse is the idea that punishment must be inflicted on autistic children when they are simply being themselves.

The unfair part is that autistic children are expected by larger society to act as if they are not autistic, and no effort is made to understand that the separation is a difference, not a problem. The same does not apply to non-autistic people, to whom society does not dictate in terms of adopting autistic behavior. Neither group can empathize with the other, but one group is expected to do so, which is simply not possible. In crude terms, and this is a generalization, non-autistic people do not care about autistic people and are not prepared to learn before criticizing or writing off autistic individuals.

Society is most certainly not inclusive, and this is the cause of the alienation, embarrassment, and isolation felt by autistic people. Bullying is common in children with autism, and the results can be tragic, considering that suicide is very often seen in autistic people. Not catering to the habits, hobbies, requirements, and differences in the function of autistic children is a big problem, as the formative years shape the rest of a child's life.

Putting the Theory Into Practice

We can't be too critical of society, bearing in mind that autism is not widely understood, and that is one of the reasons why the double empathy theory seeks to change perceptions.

The National Autistic Society has developed training programs influenced by the theory, but much more application and education are needed. We must, however, take comfort in the fact that there are ways to change perceptions and dispel ignorance.

Authors Caren Zucker and John Donovan co-wrote a New York Times best-selling book turned PBS documentary titled In a Different Key. The story reveals the tale of a reporter and the mother of a young Autistic adult son who tracked down the first person ever diagnosed with autism in the US. What she learns during her journey teaches her and the viewers an immense amount, some of which is surprising and pleasing and some of which is disheartening. In the end, the documentary leaves the viewer hopeful that society is capable of change and that we should support those individuals that may appear different from us.

Socials Skills Learning for Children

Social skills change as a child grows up. Like any person in this world, we all have strengths and weaknesses. As a very simple example, some people are good musicians; others are not but can still learn to play an instrument. In the realm of social skills, autistic children are no different. Just like teaching someone to play a musical instrument, where fluency and change of method are necessitated by progress, teaching social skills to autistic children will also change depending on the situation.

The idea is to reach a point where social skill displays become automatic. If an autistic child is working on a goal related to learning how to compromise in their relationship with peers, frustration might creep in initially. When all the nuances of how to compromise and the benefits of compromise are understood, then some real progress has been made.

Teaching social skills can be developed through games. If emotion identification is being worked on, the autistic child could be asked to call out different emotions based on picture cards. After thirty seconds, the parent or educator will pause and count the picture cards together with the child. Each time the exercise is repeated, the incentive of beating the previous score should be enough to provide fun and excitement, which is conducive to effective learning.

Without losing sight of the fact that autistic children do learn in different ways, this method is applicable to anyone. Just some of the possible goals for social skills learning are:

• Thinking in a flexible way.

• Knowing when to say what's on our minds versus when we should hold the thought in our heads.

- Understanding the concept of reading a room.

- Understanding how to adapt the how, what, and why we communicate, depending on the situation we are in or the person we are talking to.

- Understanding how and why we compromise in friendship, or at work.

- Knowing how much information to share.

- Knowing about proximity expectations.

- Understanding/using tone of voice.

Chapter 4

What Does Socializing Mean to Neurodivergent Individuals

Many neurodivergent individuals, whether children, teens, or adults, prefer spending time with other neurodivergents. This thinking also applies to neurotypicals, in that like-minded people gravitate towards each other. The result is that our friends have similar interests, are probably close in age, and are people by whom we do not feel judged. Autistic individuals are inclined not to feel judged when they interact with other autistic individuals, as that sense of alienation is not present. It does not mean that neurodivergents and neurotypicals cannot be friends. Logically, parents spend time with their autistic children, and so do educators. Those are not strictly friendships but do constitute interactions between neurotypicals and neurodivergents.

Social Thinking © Methodology

Our human brains are automatically wired to think socially. We try to make sense of our surroundings and what is going on, as per our social radar. From that point, we can figure out what to do or how to act. Our social brain works all the time, even if we are reading, watching movies, or even just observing people in a general situation without interacting. Cognition or cognitive skills can be used to understand social thinking, and three broad categories, which overlap slightly, are used to group and understand the broader concept of social thinking.

A well-respected expert on the topic is Michelle Garcia Winner, who created a company by the name of Social Thinking © over twenty-five years ago. She has contributed to several best-selling books and provides online, and in-person training about the intricacies of social interactions, the importance thereof, and the skills to develop in order to improve social and general quality of life.

Michelle defines social thinking as:

"The ability to consider your own and others' thoughts, emotions, beliefs, intentions, and knowledge to help interpret and respond to the information in your mind, and possibly through your social behavioral interactions."

The Social Thinking © Competency Model strives to teach skills via language-based metacognitive tools to help both the interventionist and the student learning. The core vocabulary used makes some concepts that are somewhat abstract seem clearer, especially when paired with great visuals. These concepts include but are not limited to flexible thinking, just me versus you thinking, social detective thinking, and thinking with your eyes, body, and brain in the group. Teaching these concepts in real-time allows for increased self-awareness and better self-monitoring for the child.

Our Meaning Maker

As the name suggests, we make meaning out of life, not in the sense of answering the big life questions, but by observing and taking in our surroundings. Loosely, you could term it "assessing what is going on." To use a rudimentary example, when crossing a road, we look for cars, and when it is safe, we walk to the other side. This isn't a social setting in terms of conversations or interactions, but it illustrates the meaning we make out of the situation. Imagination is also a convention of our meaning makers, and autistic children can struggle in group interactions at school to listen to what the educator is saying, imagine or interpret it, then put it into action.

Adaptation of Social Behavior

For example, let's take a discussion between a thirty-year-old and an eighty-year-old. The discussion will be socially different from a chat between two thirty-year-olds. The younger person would talk slowly, explain concepts simply, use less slang, and tailor the conversation to the participants. The concept goes deeper than that, though, in the worlds of neurotypicals and neurodivergents; the three important "S-words" are: self-awareness, self-monitoring, and self-control.

Social behavior is about adapting to situations. In life, there are interrupters, including autistic children, but we can learn to hear the other person out before speaking.

As a brief aside, it is interesting that neurodivergents and neurotypicals make exactly the same social faux pas, even though the social experience can be very differently experienced.

Using Social Skills

We all want to feel included and liked by friends, family, and even strangers, which means that employing social skills in a way that serves ourselves and others is important. It can be challenging for autistic children to understand how to give the other person or people the desired emotional experience. Due to this, autistic children may be perceived as anti-social or self-absorbed when, in fact, they are just displaying differences. At the end of the day, social skills are taught to most children; some are better at socializing than others, but with constant teaching, autistic children can thrive in social settings that may have seemed overwhelming in the beginning.

What Exactly Are Social Skills?

We could probably create an exhaustive list of what social skills actually are. However, in a broad sense, the following five categorizations can be seen as umbrella terms under which the larger scope of skills fall:

- Social awareness

- Social cognition

- Social communication

- Social motivation

- Autistic mannerisms

As we know, neurodivergents interpret the world differently, and the old-fashioned thinking that autistic individuals lack social skills is outdated and incorrect.

Social "Norms" and Cues

Having a quick conversation with a server when ordering coffee will probably go something like this:

Server: Good morning; how are you?

Customer: I'm fine, thanks. May I please have a medium coffee with extra cream?

Server: Yes, sure.

Customer: Thank you, and have a nice day.

Server: You too.

In this scenario, when the customer is asked how they are doing, they don't go into details about their work issues or their recent holiday. The exchange is quick, polite, and pretty generic. An autistic person in that situation may start telling the server their life story, and it makes perfect sense. The server asks the question, so the autistic individual answers it, but the social norm is generally a quick, polite, frivolous exchange.

Take a scenario where an autistic person is on a bus next to a stranger, and the stranger strikes up a conversation. Perhaps the stranger says, "Tell me about yourself." That is a social cue that informs the autistic person that he or she may talk about themselves. The polite thing to do would be to finish answering the question and then ask it back to the other person. That skill can be taught by explaining that a conversation should flow both ways and that this type of interaction is vastly different from the server example.

Sarcasm and Humor

Some people, neurotypical or neurodivergent, struggle with sarcasm, but using sarcasm can be a good icebreaker or a way of lightening the mood. Autistic children tend to be very literal and have trouble understanding sarcasm, which may create the impression of disinterest or irritability. Although not strictly sarcastic, the "Why did the chicken cross the road? To get to the other side" (joke). If interpreted literally, is not funny at all. An autistic child will probably think that it is stupid because it is logical.

Masking can also come into play, where a child learns to laugh at a certain point but hasn't actually identified the sarcasm. Some may argue that this is a good thing because the child will feel included. However, if the child is taught how sarcasm works, then there is a good chance that inclusion will be a result of understanding the use of sarcasm and actually enjoying the humor.

Manners

It is the responsibility of parents to teach their children manners, which can be challenging for autistic children. The school also plays a role, but we can't forget that if manners are not understood, it takes a lot more time and effort to learn them. This is another social convention that doesn't really separate neurotypicals and neurodivergents. Saying "please" and "thank you" are the very basics. However, you will often see parents constantly reminding their children to use those words. It is a very simple example, but the point is that repetition is a tool to be used with any child. The difficulty is that autistic children may miss the cues, but identifying when to stand up to greet somebody, open a door, or participate equally in a conversation, etc., are all teachable skills.

Back and Forth Conversation

During conversations, body language is used extensively, so not only talking but also conducting our body language is the correct way to suit the situation. Often, autistic children will shy away from talking, which can be perceived as a lack of interest. However, the reality is that an autistic child may feel overwhelmed in a conversation and, for that reason, exercise non-participation.

Initiating a Conversation

This can be practiced at home, and like anything, repetition is the key. Autistic children will often be interested in, perhaps even obsessed with, a specific area of interest.

In the previously mentioned Netflix series, Atypical, the lead protagonist has a fascination with penguins and their Antarctic environment. He reads about them, draws them, and brings them up often in conversation. As an autistic boy in his late teens, it is fantastic that he has a subject that he loves talking about. However, the other person in the conversation may want to talk about different things, which is the way that a back-and-forth discussion should play out.

There are five main conversational skills, among others, that can be developed when working with an autistic child to prepare them for real-world conversations:

- Picking a topic

- Starting the dialogue

- Taking turns to speak

- Asking questions and answering questions

- Ending the conversation at the right point

In a role-play situation, the autistic child must pick a topic that they are interested in. As it is an accurate example, I will use the interest in penguins from Atypical. This is not an actual conversation but a hypothetical one. ND refers to neurodiverse, and NT refers to neurotypical:

ND initiates a conversation with a new child at school.

ND: Hello, my name is ND. What is your name?

NT: My name is NT; nice to meet you.

ND: Nice to meet you too. Do you like penguins?

NT: I don't really know much about them.

ND: Would you like me to tell you about them?

NT: Yes, if you would like to.

*ND talks for a few minutes on penguins; an appropriate amount of time.

ND: Do you like any animals?

NT: Yes, my family actually has a small farm.

*NT talks for an appropriate time.

ND: I would like to excuse myself, please. I have a class to get to. It was nice talking to you.

NT: Yes, it was nice talking to you. Maybe we can talk more tomorrow.

ND: I'd like that.

The above is a very summarized version of a role-play exercise, with the goal of limiting the amount of time that the autistic child spends on their area of interest and giving the other party an equal amount of time to speak about their interest. The open-ended questions promote the flow of the conversation. Politeness and ending the conversation at the right time are also part of the exercise. These types of role-plays can then be applied in the outside world and assist in developing mutual friendships that are a component of a better quality of life.

Visual tools and cues, such as a drawing that shows the child how much to add to a conversation (a ruler or measuring cup would be an appropriate representation) visuals to help a child know when and how to change the subject when to pause, and when and how to ask follow-up questions (the stop and go of a traffic light would be a good visual representation). Getting a child to know the difference between. When to "say it" and when to "think it" can be taught by pairing photos of feeling faces with practice phrases such as "I hate your new haircut" paired with a photo of a surprised face.

Communication

As we all know, poor communication generally has poor results, whether in romantic relationships, work relationships, or relationships with friends. Sometimes, autistic children find it a challenge to put all the components of communication together, so manners may slip, or the mutuality of conversation may be forgotten.

Looking Directly at Others

Maintaining eye contact can be extremely stressful and anxiety-inducing for autistic children. It does not translate into not caring what the other person is saying, but it can inhibit picking up cues and reading the conversation. The jury is out on whether or not to teach autistic children to make eye contact because it may feel forced and will then be a major source of distress in a conversational environment. We look at a face for many reasons—there is INFORMATION in the eyes, eyebrows, and face overall. We "reference" for information, permission, and shared enjoyment. My neurotypical 6-month-old son saw a butterfly when he was looking out the window. He referenced me (by looking at me) to share the joy of his discovery, and because he couldn't speak at the time, I gave him the words with a smile: "Yes, you see the butterfly, and you want to see if mommy saw it too; I do see it!... It's flying in our yard."

There are a variety of "silent" games we can play that teach children they must look in order for the fun game to continue. During the lessons or games, we don't try to achieve eye contact by asking for eye contact or calling their name. A quick glance at the speaker is all that is required for the game to continue. We need to remember that when doing eye contact exercises, it is important to teach WHY eye contact is necessary. If there is a reason behind something, it will make more sense to put it into action.

Not Responding to Being Called

Being easily distracted or zoning out when being spoken to can appear rude, but many autistic children and adults, especially those with ADHD, sometimes don't even realize that someone is trying to get their attention. We have all been in a situation where we are engrossed in a book or completely focused on a TV show, and we don't hear or subconsciously block out our name being called. The same thing applies to autism and can happen mid-conversation. Active listening exercises are very helpful. In a mock conversation, you point out to your autistic child that they have allowed a distraction to creep in. To work on this, use very short bouts of conversation, take a break, throw a ball around for a few minutes, then go back to chatting. The result of our readiness for longer, engaging conversations will come very slowly, but it will come.

Parents often become confused when their toddler doesn't respond to their name, yet when they sing a familiar tune, the child turns around toward the source of the sound. One reason they may not be responding is that they need to know that their name represents who they are and that calling them means you want them to look at you. Another reason they don't refer to you when you call them could be that they are more motivated by what is happening around them (the environment) or inside them (sensory). Some toddlers have receptive language (understanding) like a 2–3-month-old child. That being said, music is processed in a different part of the brain than the part involved in language use or understanding.

Not Engaging in Small Talk

Small talk can be very generic and awkward at the best of times. Autistic children tend to find small talk boring and pointless, so this skill and the reasons behind it need to be taught. If you are in an elevator with someone, the atmosphere can feel uncomfortable, and short bits of conversation like "the weather is nice" or "did you have a good weekend?" can fill that awkward space. Just like the chicken crossing the road, an autistic child will very likely see this as an obvious and unnecessary statement. Role-playing to teach different types of small talk in differing environments is good preparation in terms of understanding and employing small talk when required.

Continuing to Talk About Something That Other Participants in the Conversation Are Not Interested in social conventions dictate that in conversations, we sometimes have to entertain a topic that the other person is talking about, even if we find it boring. Using social tact, we may want to change the subject and go about it in a way that fits the conversation, such as picking up on something specific, making a comment, and directing the discussion towards another topic. It is, however, easy to miss the social cues when we are talking about something that the other participant finds uninteresting. These types of social cues are important to developing a conversation that provides stimulation to everyone involved. I gave the earlier example of the neurodivergent character from the series Atypical, who has a love for everything penguin. Nature is something that many people find interesting, but if only one aspect or one animal is a continuous topic, it will get boring. For your autistic child, it is necessary to get the balance right. In role-playing conversations, let your child talk for too long on one topic, then stop him or her. Do the same when it is your turn to talk, and note when he or she starts to get bored. The more practice there is, the more understanding and comfortable discussions will become with peers.

Relationships

All of the social skills that we have dealt with come together in the development of relationships. Often, when we hear the word "relationship," we think of a romantic one, but as I mentioned earlier, relationships take many forms. I would highly recommend the Netflix series Love on the Spectrum. The show aims to show that autistic people are all different in terms of their abilities, likes, and desires in a relationship. It showcases their desire for connection and some of the obstacles they encounter along the way. Parents, friends, and educators that understand and assist autistic individuals are interviewed, and one really gets a sense of how much love and care goes around. We all need love and care! Let's take a look at non-romantic relationships for now.

Levels of Friendship

Friendships improve and enrich our lives, but it can be tough for autistic children to initiate long-standing friendships. If we are not sure of what a friendship actually is, then making friends maybe even more challenging. Teaching autistic children about friendship and allowing them to understand the different levels of friendship gives them a practical sense of what it means to be friends with someone. Take social media, for example: Many people have thousands of Facebook friends but only talk to a fraction of those people. Often, we meet someone once, receive a friend request, accept it, and never talk to that "friend." That doesn't translate well into real-life, face-to-face friendships, but there are four commonly regarded levels of friendship. If an autistic children can be taught the differences, then they can identify what friendship means to the other person and what level of friendship can be attained.

The book Why Johnny doesn't flap: NT (neurotypical) is OK by Clay, and Gail Morton features an autistic child narrating his thoughts and feelings about his neurotypical friend's odd behavior, such as not flapping to show excitement to the audience. It's a book all about perspective... I love it! We need more books like this, and they need to be read to all children in all classes.

Acquaintances

People can have several acquaintances; a neighbor is an often-used example. You may know your neighbor's name and what work he or she does, but aside from polite exchanges when you happen to see each other over the fence, you don't engage in lengthy conversations. The same could be said for interactions with the library clerk or the lifeguard at a local pool—anyone with whom you have a very small amount of small talk on semi-regular occasions.

Casual Friends

Casual friends are more than acquaintances, and the obvious difference is that casual friends make plans to meet as opposed to just having a conversation if and when they run into each other. Casual friends may enjoy going to see a movie together or playing catch at the park. Usually, there is a shared interest, let's say hiking, around which the friendship is based. Discussions are likely to be limited in a "personal life" sense, and a casual friend is someone that you would probably not share about the intricacies of your problems or issues. It could be argued that most close friendships start out as casual friendships and grow from there, but of course, some casual friendships remain that way without evolving.

Close Friends

Close friends will probably see each other more often and know a great deal about each other. Emotional support, guidance, and advice are all characteristics of a close friendship. You feel comfortable enough with that person to share a lot of information about yourself, your life, other relationships, and vice versa. There is no specific amount of time that needs to pass in order to become close friends with someone, but it comes down to the frequency of interaction.

Here are a few more characteristics of what one would call a close friendship:

- You are happy to help and want to help each other.

- You do not fear judgment when asking for advice.

- You respect and appreciate each other.

- You do not feel a need to mask or camouflage.

- You empathize rather than criticize.

Intimate Friends

An intimate friendship is only a slight step up from a close friendship. All the same tenets as above apply, but essentially, there is no topic too sensitive or intimate to discuss. Intimate friends feel completely safe in each other's company and want to spend as much time as possible together. An intimate friend is a best friend, and yes, one can have more than one best friend.

Friendships in Autism

The friendship levels are the same for everyone. However, for autistic children, the ability to identify what information to share, what to say, and how to say it are the difficult parts, as explored in the social skills section. Nobody enjoys rejection, which is a real fear in any potential relationship, and as is the case with autistic children, alienation is a possibility.

Encouraging friendships between neurodivergents and neurotypicals is a double-edged sword, largely because neurotypicals can have a limited understanding of the differences, especially the fact that the initial stages of a relationship can be scary for neurodivergents. There are ways to slowly integrate and take a relationship from an acquaintance to an intimate friend, but it has to be treated delicately. One of the ways in which friendships can be formed is through sports.

Such is based on a mutual interest as well as the inclusive feeling of working together to score a goal or make a touchdown. For example: Any shared interest, like art, music, or video games, works to begin a friendship. More education needs to happen in schools so that neurotypicals are more patient, kind, and understanding. Kids are not weird if they aren't "just like you."

I also like the idea of neurodivergents befriending other neurodivergents as well. This dynamic works especially well for the parent, as it takes a lot less stress off them to sit and chat with another mom, knowing if their child does something unexpected, it wouldn't be too big of a deal.

Sports and Autism

Even though team sports provide a way to engage positively with other autistic children, the fear of letting a teammate down or playing badly might be present. Individual sports can also be daunting, but the improvement and application of social skills can be achieved. In terms of the most popular sports that autistic children enjoy, team sports, in general, come in fourth place, so there appears to be a propensity to favor individual sports in a group setting. Here are the top three:

Swimming

Studies have shown that swimming is the number one preferred sport for autistic children. Apart from health benefits, swimming is of great assistance in improving gross motor control in autistic children.

Horseback Riding

First off, equine therapy can teach autistic children to form connections with animals. If one struggles with human relationships, developing a bond with a horse, for instance, can educate an autistic child as to the way relationships feel. Like all sports, there is a fitness element, and being outside can't do any harm.

Martial Arts

Martial arts is about discipline, and as we know, autistic children often like specific rules as well. A 2019 study, referenced below, found that after a thirteen-week mixed martial arts program, autistic children of school-going age showed large improvements in self-regulation, focus, and attention (Phung, J. Goldberg, W., 2019).

Appropriate Reactions

As I have said before, social conventions tell us how to react appropriately in different contexts. Very often, we do not comply with those social conventions, but we are aware that they are there. Raising one's voice in a discussion or failing to help someone in need are small examples. So, parents and educators need to explain to autistic children what the most productive reactions are in social settings that may be unpleasant, awkward, or unfounded.

Bullying and/or Rejection

Bullying appears to be on the rise and is something that most humans have dealt with in their lives. It also appears that when school bullies grow up and reach maturity levels, they often regret their actions. Being bullied can leave lasting emotional scars, and with maturity, victims of bullies very often fail to shake off the memories and the feelings associated with their former school bullies.

Dr. Lori Ernsperger, Ph.D., has been instrumental in addressing bullying and the ways in which it can be approached. She owns and runs Autism and Behavioral Consulting ©, and provides workshops for educators and parents, especially on the "three R's" to combat bullying:

Recognize

Parents and educators of autistic children are under no illusions that bullying is frequent but often not recognized. The "know it when you see it" mantra can be applied. However, children still need to be taught to recognize bullying. Getting into an argument with a friend is probably not bullying; being pushed around or harassed by a classmate is probably bullying. The intention is the thing to look out for.

Respond

Anyone who sees bullying taking place has the responsibility to act in the correct way. If a friend is being bullied, the primal reaction may be to beat up the bully, but as the saying goes, "two wrongs don't make a right." Everyone who is involved with children, from the school bus driver to the school principal to the hall monitors, needs to be aware of bullying. The next step, if you are unable to harness the bullying situation, is to report it.

Report

Educators are taught how to address bullying, and even as a parent, you should report bullying to teachers, therapists, or other persons who are there to act in the best interests of your autistic child. By way of a quick Google search, you can find many organizations and societies that assist with bullying prevention. There is no harm in reporting it to as many helping hands as possible as long as it is positively addressed.

Empathy and Autism

Empathy is the ability to identify with another person's situation and share the feelings that they are experiencing. Our ability to empathize is drawn largely from having felt what the other person is feeling before, also called "lived experiences." There was a school of thought, and perhaps there still is, that autistic individuals lack empathy. However, very often, the case is that empathy is not overtly obvious because such individuals do not know how to show it; that doesn't mean that it isn't there. This is merely a difference and not a problem or abnormality. In fact, it is believed that approximately 15% of people do not feel empathy at all (Hall, J. Leary, M.). In autistic children, role play is an excellent method of teaching the ways in which to show empathy through listening, talking, and physical contact. Sometimes a simple hug can go a long way toward illustrating empathy without words.

Chapter 5

How to Use Words Constructively

Words are so powerful, and for far too long, terms such as "special needs," "high or low functioning," and "challenging behavior" have been used when referring to autistic and ADHD children. Humans should be kind to each other, and for that to work, we need to reassess the type of language we use to describe differences in individuals. One can effect change through language use, and it can be a slow process. Because alienating and insulting terms have been in use for so long, change does not happen immediately. Education must accompany change; if an individual uses language that they do not even know is negative and unproductive, then a change will never take place. In this chapter, we will look at language and the problems with certain terms, and expand upon the outdated versus the new.

High-Functioning and Low-Functioning

These categorizations are not medical terms and are, to a

certain extent, self-explanatory. If we change the context completely, take a step back, and do a bit of analysis, we can refer to a "high-functioning or functional alcoholic." That would be someone who has a drinking problem but holds down a good job, maintains fitness, has healthy relationships, and operates as if they were not an alcoholic. Obviously, drinking too much is a big problem, but calling someone in that situation "high-functioning" is not offensive. Take someone who has the same problem with alcohol but is in and out of jobs, can't hold down relationships, and is not a positive asset to society. "Low-functioning" is an appropriate term, but don't forget that a person like this is causing low functionality themselves. In autism, it is merely a case of differences: different hobbies, different ways of expressing oneself, and different ways of interacting. In life, people are good at some things and not so good at others. All it amounts to is being different.

The term "high functioning" can be problematic for some people. A former student of mine who is now an adult told me recently that because he was labeled high-functioning, many of his needs went unmet. He had a lot of sensory needs in the areas of vision and touch that were not addressed. This made his high school experience not just unpleasant but almost unbearable at times. Accommodations on his Individualized Educational Plan (IEP) could have quickly and easily made his life much more bearable.

High-Functioning Autism

That being said, self-advocating often falls on deaf ears, as general education teachers (another not-so-nice term) and exceptional student educators don't always have a good understanding of things like unregulated sensory systems and how significant they can be in everyday life. Let alone in a setting where learning is supposed to be taking place.

Although not the correct term, we need to explore it a bit. What follows are the characteristics of high-functioning autistic children. Some refer to them as "symptoms," but as we know, that is also not the correct term, so let's look at the characteristics that are shown by autistic children:

Routines

Following a specific routine is a good thing, and it is often observed that autistic children enjoy routines. For instance, waking up at a certain time, having the same thing for breakfast, always sitting in the same place, and watching only a few shows on TV. Just think of people who don't have routines and the stress that it can cause. One downside of a lack of routine is the struggle with punctuality. However, following the same or similar procedure every day allows for order to be maintained, which lends itself to experiencing less anxiety and feeling in control.

Specific Interests

For instance, if an autistic child is interested in dinosaurs, they will watch all the shows that they can find on dinosaurs, read books on the topic, chat about it often, have dinosaur toys, wear dinosaur clothes, and absorb themselves in everything dinosaur. There is often not a huge difference between neurodivergents and neurotypicals. For instance, children can become obsessive (in a good way) about learning a musical instrument, whether they are neurodiverse or not.

Food Habits

Autistic individuals often have very particular opinions and behaviors around food. This is sometimes linked to the desire for routine and consists of separating food on one's plate; veggies on this side, meat on that side, gravy in a bowl next to the plate, and so on. A reason behind this could be the different ways in which autistic individuals experience their senses. Avoiding foods with smells that are unpleasant or overwhelming, such as garlic, is a noticeable food habit, in addition to avoiding foods that are a particular color. The texture of food in one's mouth can play a big role in the acceptance or rejection of food, which could be why "neurodivergents" may prefer to only eat a few types of food.

Social Anxiety in Communicative Settings

This goes back to missing social cues and the distractions involved. However, as addressed earlier, role-playing and explanations of how to deal with social communication are tools that can be used to reduce anxiety.

Being Overwhelmed

Take a restaurant setting where knives are scraping plates, children are screeching, and music is being played. This type of combinational sensory overload can cause panic attacks or meltdowns facilitated by feelings of overwhelm. Alienation and feelings of being different in a negative way can follow, as well as stares from strangers and displays of judgment. We have to remember that being overwhelmed is so common in people, but the reaction is different in autistic children. We must also remember what overwhelm looks and feels like. When compared to neurotypical children, it can be quite different for autistic children.

Low-Functioning Autism

Like high-functioning autism, this is also not the correct term, but we still need to explore it a bit. Known nowadays as "level three autism," children require much more support from parents and educators. In this sense, autistic children may have trouble speaking and can be difficult to understand. Generally, the support needed involves reminding them—to put it colloquially—to brush their teeth, when to eat, and when to change clothes. Children who are level three autistic struggle with learning and will be unlikely to have a job as they progress through life, partially because social interactions are exceptionally intimidating. Like all children, they need love, care, and support.

Parents obviously need to be the advocates and voices for these children, taking into account the following high support needs:

- The need for vigilant supervision

- Non-speaking

- No interest in using AAC

- Does not point or sign during or after the toddler-aged years

- Does not imitate

- Permanent scars from self-injury

- Higher risk for abuse by strangers

- No concept of danger

- High elopement risk

- Sensory dysregulation

- Very little to zero self-care skills

- Disrobes regularly and/or unexpectedly

- Not toilet trained after the expected age

- Uses a bottle sippy cup after the expected age

The term "high support needs" is also a preferred term for "low-functioning." However, many parents fear the change in terminology as they are concerned about services (medical and therapeutic) not being available if we view ASD as "just a brain difference." Insurance companies won't pay for services if they are not perceived as medical.

Non-speaking doesn't mean non-thinking. Some non-speaking autistic adults are presented with AAC, such as an "alphabet letter board," and can suddenly communicate some pretty mind-blowing messages after decades of silence.

Levels of Autism

It is time to throw the terms "high-functioning" and "low-functioning" out of the window, as should be the case, and look at the three levels, the third of which we dealt with briefly above.

Level One

Otherwise known as the mildest form of autism and the one that we have discussed most in this book. This level of autism requires support, but to a limited degree, and is characterized by the following:

- Difficulty initiating social interactions

- Organization and planning challenges

- Missing social cues

Level Two

One could say this is the middle-of-the-road level and requires substantial parental and educational support, characterized by:

- Extreme focus on special interests

- Requiring the implementation of concrete rules

- Repetitive behaviors (talking about one subject excessively)

Level Three

This type of experience as an autistic child requires very substantial support, characterized by the following:

- Difficulties with communication, both verbal and nonverbal

- Experiencing greater distress in anxiety-inducing situations

- Rapid change of focus and/or activities

The autism spectrum is not linear, with level one at one end and level three at the other. Trying to describe it visually, the spectrum looks more like a web where traits occur on a continuum. A person could be highly verbal but have low sensory needs. They could also be non-speaking with a high need for routines. We should never assume anything at all regarding the intelligence of an autistic person, no matter their level. Levels of support needs and cognitive abilities are not dependent variables.

Limitations of Autism Spectrum Disorder (Difference)

Imagine wanting to do something but just not being able to do it, and your brain does not allow you to execute the task. One can try to press through and then experience burnout. This happens to neurotypicals as well, but neurodivergents experience this phenomenon on a heightened level. ADHD individuals are particularly affected and will often get a task almost finished but can't quite complete it. Like any limitation, this can be overcome or at least managed. Don't forget that autistic and ADHD children have strengths and weaknesses in different areas. Some may need support at school but little or no support at home. The same applies to social interactions. If someone is aware of what limits them, that aspect can be worked on or managed to the point where such limitations become less and less prevalent.

Medical Model vs. Social Model

In a physical sense, the medical model sees a disability as a problem that the disabled person has. It is not seen as an issue for anyone but that person. In the case of a physical disability, let's say that we have someone who is paralyzed from the waist down and uses a wheelchair to get around. Stairs provide an obvious problem, and the medical model sees the "problem" as the wheelchair and not the stairs. In this model, the focus is on the paralysis and not the person and his or her differences.

The social model would see the steps as the barrier for the person in the wheelchair instead of seeing the wheelchair as the problem. If a person has different needs, whether physically or otherwise, the disability only comes into play when that person is excluded due to their differences. Removing difficulties faced due to differences is the responsibility of society, and this forms part of changing perceptions of autism and ADHD.

The medical model was conceived in 1951 by T. Parsons, and as one can imagine, back then, very little was known about autism. The model was more physically disability-focused and received criticism for the potential alienation of disabled individuals due to their "special needs" and the alienation that such individuals would feel. If one applies the model to autistic people, the word "disability" should not be used. In fact, the entire medical model should not be used, as autistic individuals are not disabled; they are just different in terms of their experiences and actions.

Shortcomings of the Medical Model

As noted above, the medical model is outdated and uses language that is neither constructive nor positive. It affects the way autistic children see themselves and has the potential to be a hindrance to positive development. Its shortcomings specific to autism and ADHD are:

- Giving a child and others the impression or belief that there is something wrong with the child.

- Creation of negative labels.

- The main focus becomes impairment, and the ordinary needs that the child has are deflected away.

- A sense of exclusion.

Positives of the Social Model

It is widely agreed that the social model is the most effective one that provides for positive growth by:

- Recognizing the child's value.

- Setting out barriers and solutions to overcome those barriers.

- Making the outcome the main focus.

- Nurturing relationships and needs every day.
- Creating a sense of inclusion.

Specialized Care

As a parent, your needs take a back seat when raising an autistic child, and in the early years, it can be hard to figure it all out. It can be difficult to know what to do or where to find educators and therapists who will cater to the needs of your autistic child. The IEP, or Individualized Education Plan, was designed to help parents of autistic children by giving them the extra support they needed. The Individualized Educational Plan, legislated by the US government, applies to the public school system. The early intervention (EI) program is available before a child is eligible for an IEP, from birth to the age of three.

THE INDIVIDUALIZED EDUCATIONAL PLAN

Some children qualify for an IEP as early as age three. As part of the pre-K–12 school system, an IEP lays out the special education instruction, supports, and services a student needs to thrive in school. The IEP can include both modifications and accommodations for kids with brain-based learning challenges. If your child qualifies for an IEP, remember that as a parent, you are part of the team of people who help develop the IEP. Your thoughts, opinions, questions, and concerns matter. Parents and IEP teams meet to flesh out a plan to provide support best suited to the child. As a parent, you can't quite tell the IEP team what to do, but there is a framework within which you can collaborate. IEP aims to be very inclusive (O'Shea, 2022).

Some examples of the many possible IEP accommodations:

- Reduced assignments and homework.

- Chunking of longer assignments.

- Preferential seating near the point of instruction.

- 50% additional time for tests and quizzes

- Noise-canceling for loud areas, such as hallways and lunchrooms.

- Warning and preparation when challenges are anticipated.

504 PLANS

In contrast to an IEP, which focuses on the educational benefits and often includes direct services such as speech or occupational therapy, the 504 Plan of the Federal Rehabilitation Act, ensures a student has equitable access to a learning environment. Accommodations of a 504 Plan are typically grouped into four categories: presentation, response, setting, and timing and scheduling.

Workshops

If an autistic child's classmates can gain information about autism and the reasons why neurotypicals and neurodivergents are different in disposition and experience, then inclusion is more achievable. There are so many opportunities to educate in this way, and it may be as simple as a parent or educator running a short workshop at an autistic child's school. With understanding comes inclusion, and as human beings, we should not criticize or pass judgment on things we don't understand.

High Sensory Needs

In a public or school situation, it can sometimes be a challenge to regulate different sensory needs, but there are ways to do so. Noise-canceling headphones for autistic children who are particularly sensitive to combinations of surrounding sounds have been shown to be effective. Monitoring odors in the classroom for less stressful smell experiences, wearing light-regulating glasses for reduction of heightened sensitivity to color or brightness, and controlling lunchtime meals for taste sensitivity treatment are all great ways of catering to the personal requirements of autistic children.

Self-Harm

Often in autistic children, self-harm is observed, but it is not about seeking out the pain but rather blocking out the overwhelming sensations created by sensory overload. Self-harm most certainly is not self-stimming, but the principle is similar, whereby a distraction is created as a coping mechanism for placement in an uncomfortable or anxiety-evoking setting. It is important to note that self-harm is always a result of something, and as we know, autistic individuals often also have mental health issues, such as depression. Cutting is often something that diagnosed depressives do to release emotional pain. However, cutting or other forms of self-harm could perhaps be categorized as mental illnesses themselves.

Self-harm has been observed in autistic children as a means of regulating sensory arousal. Most often, the intention is not to induce pain, and sometimes autistic children who seek out sensory arousal do not even realize that their actions, such as scratching themselves or hitting their heads against a wall, are pain-inducing activities.

A functional behavior assessment (FBA) should be conducted by a certified behavior analyst to determine the function and cause of the behavior (internal or environmental factors maintaining the behavior). During the process of developing an FBA, data is recorded, monitoring the antecedent (what occurs before the behavior) and the consequence (what occurs after the behavior). Once the results are analyzed, a behavior intervention plan (BIP) is written to change or improve the outcome for the student exhibiting the behavior judged to be harmful or causing injury.

Life Expectancy

Life expectancy in autism is affected by environmental and genetic risk factors. Unfortunately, long-term outcomes regarding independent living, education, and employment for autistic individuals do not lend themselves to a positive life expectancy. Autistic children are more susceptible to death as a result of physical injuries, and shockingly, the life expectancy of an autistic individual is only 39.5 to 58 years (Sala, R. et al, n.d.). Suffocation, asphyxiation, and drowning are three of the more common ways in which autistic individuals lose their lives.

In terms of drowning, anyone with an autistic child who lives anywhere near water (think pool, lake, canal) must consider teaching their child to swim, or at least to flip and float, when they are as young as possible (1–2 years of age). Since elopement is such a challenge for families, the risk of a child wandering into a body of water and drowning is real. It is the most common fatal injury among autistic children.

Suicide is reported to be higher among autistic individuals as opposed to neurotypicals. Taking one's own life is not a physical or medical condition, but considering that autism and mental health can be closely related, higher suicide rates are understandable.

The tragedy is that the alienation and loneliness that are often imposed by society's treatment of autistic people are causes of depression, which in turn can lead to suicide.

In terms of general health, epilepsy is more common in people with autism, and epileptic seizures are a contributor to premature deaths. Heart disease and several intestinal ailments are further contributors. If we think about it logically, the stressors and near-constant presence of possible unpleasant situations causing extreme anxiety are not good for cognitive and physical health. Brain inflammation, strokes, and diabetes are collateral contributors to premature death in this sense as well.

The Puzzle Piece and the Infinity Symbol

The puzzle-piece symbol is definitely outdated and is considered offensive by many. This is not always the case, but there is broad agreement on the topic. The puzzle piece symbol was created by Gerald Gasson of the National Autistic Society (NAS) in the United Kingdom. The year was 1963, and a crying child was depicted next to the puzzle piece. NAS spokesperson Helen Allison was quoted as saying:

"The puzzle piece is so effective because it tells us something about autism: our children are handicapped by a puzzling condition; this isolates them from normal human contact, and they do not "fit in." The suggestion of a weeping child is a reminder that autistic people do suffer from their handicap." (Autisticalex, 2014).

Reading such a statement is very frustrating, but one has to remember that 1963 was a much less informed and much more ignorant time period. The designers, of course, were non-autistic individuals speaking on behalf of autistic individuals, but they were unaware of and not well-versed in the ins and outs of autism. The offense was not intended; however, as time passed, the reasons for the offense became clearer. Though many of their behaviors are initially not understandable to everyone, which could technically be looked at as "puzzling," the symbol is overall outdated and judged by many to be inappropriate.

Autistic people are not puzzles to be figured out, and that view needs to be banished.

The rainbow infinity symbol that represents neurodiversity and the golden-colored symbol for autism are much more appropriate. Surprisingly, they only became associated with autism in 2018. Popular opinion is that the symbol represents the diversity of the spectrum and of autistic individuals. In a sense, humanity can be represented by the infinity symbol, but it is particularly appropriate for neurodiverse and autistic people. It promotes the ideas of understanding, sharing, and the involvement of neurotypicals in supporting autistic individuals.

Is Autism Just a Neurotype?

The term "neuro" is a medical one that refers to nerves or the human nervous system, meaning that the term "neurotype" is a bit of a misnomer because type does not mean typical. It really isn't just semantics, as it may appear, because the word "typical" describes a person or thing with characteristics that are widely shared or most common in that grouping of people or things.

We know that the word "neurodiverse" is used in language about autism, but being neurodiverse does not necessarily mean that one is autistic. A child may have ADHD without being autistic but still, fit into the neurodiverse category. Other neurological differences make individuals neurodiverse. For example, consider tourette's, depression, schizophrenia, or dyslexia. Autism can present in conjunction with the examples, but being autistic does make someone a neurotype. Neurodiversity is the recognition of differences in the way in which autistic people experience life, but the term is not solely descriptive of autism.

We do need to recognize autism for what it is, and to illustrate that it is not just a neurotype, here is the definition as per the American Psychological Association (APA) definition:

"Autism Spectrum Disorder referred to any one of a group of disorders with an onset typically occurring during the preschool years and characterized by difficulties with social communication and social interaction and restricted and repetitive patterns in behaviors, interests, and activities."

Late Identification of ASD

Most autistic individuals are identified as children. However, there are cases of autistic individuals only being diagnosed as adults. If you think or suspect that you may be on the spectrum. you may indeed be autistic, but have very low support needs. However, your quality of life can be improved after being diagnosed in very similar ways to the support provided to autistic children, as discussed in this book.

There are signs that can be used as identifiers for autistic adults, for example:

- Finding it difficult to participate in conversations.

- Being unable to relate to other people's thoughts, words, and experiences.

- Making noises in situations or places where quiet is expected.
- Using the same tone and manner of speaking in every situation, whether vastly different or not.
- Struggling to form close or meaningful friendships.

The good thing about getting a diagnosis is that you can begin to understand yourself better, including the way you relate to the world. If you know why you react in this way or behave in this way, then you can work on measures to combat anxiety or discomfort. You can find support through groups, therapists, or family, with the ongoing goal of improving your quality of life. We all want the best quality of life possible, whether we are adults, children, neurodiverse, or neurotypical.

Chapter 6

The Spectrum of Feelings

As a parent, when you receive a diagnosis and find out that your child is autistic, a variety of feelings may follow. It can be an up-and-down experience, with anger, validation, relief, confusion, and fear. Age, mindset, knowledge, and education will have an effect on how one responds to the diagnosis, but the hope is that the outcome is positive and allows parents to facilitate the support that their autistic child requires. In this chapter, we will look at ways in which to prepare for the diagnosis by delving into the different emotional experiences.

Receiving the Diagnosis

Although receiving a diagnosis is overwhelming, it is a good thing, but often there will be doubt as to the accuracy of the diagnosis. Your child is still your child after the diagnosis, so there is no actual change. However, knowing that your child is autistic should set the wheels in motion in terms of getting as much information as possible. Revealing the diagnosis to teachers, fellow parents, and family is a personal choice but highly recommended. This is a case of putting the focus on the "change of mindset," which is a big but achievable thing. You need to view the diagnosis as a positive starting point from which you can give your child the right kind of support and love that they need to have a good life. Everything becomes a learning opportunity, from crossing the road to having a polite discussion to practicing skills to alleviate anxiety-inducing experiences. The initial path forward from that line could be a difficult one, and there are a few largely recognized emotions that may follow.

Fear

Whether you are an adult who has just received a diagnosis or the parent of a newly identified autistic child, you may become scared. Questions like, "What now?" "Do I need to change/does my child need to change?" or "What will other people think?" may start flying around in your head, and you could have a notion of not knowing what to do. There is nothing wrong with this at all, and you can start to unpack everything, identify one fear at a time, and then address that fear before turning it into something positive, which needs positive action. You can look at it as if you were walking into a pitch-dark room and were afraid of what might be inside. When you put the light on and discover that there is nothing in the room to be fearful of, your fear is now baseless. So, shine some light on your fear(s) and move forward.

Relief

When you find answers to questions you have been asking

about why your child is out of sorts, throws what people perceive as tantrums, or is highly sensitive in seemingly innocuous settings, a huge sense of relief is a possibility. Receiving a diagnosis that your child is autistic provides many answers to your questions and, again, is like a new starting point.

Disgust

This applies more to adults receiving their own diagnosis, and the reason is because of the negative stigma surrounding Autism Spectrum Disorder. You may have been called "strange" or

"weird" when you were growing up, and getting diagnosed can trigger feelings that you are a strange or weird person. That is most certainly not the case; differences do not mean that there is something wrong with you. People diagnosed with depression often display disgust at themselves, and it is also stigma related. Unfortunately, human nature is to judge, and that includes judging ourselves, but in these cases, it is society's fault. As a parent of an autistic child, you may develop a "Why me?" or "Why my family?" attitude, and while this is understandable, it is not good, so if it happens, then try not to dwell on it for too long. To help with this, work on acknowledging that your life is going to be different. Feel those feelings and determine what it will take for you to be the best mom, dad, friend, and teacher you can be.

Regret

You may be inclined to look back and chastise yourself for having handled your child in a certain way, or that you would have done things differently had you known that your child was autistic a year or two prior. It's not your fault; you must move forward with your child's best interests at heart.

Acceptance

Acceptance will come, and when it does, the negative feelings and emotions will no longer exist. You can then pay clear attention to your child's support needs, acknowledge their strengths and weaknesses, do some real research, seek out help where you need it, and allow your child to live his or her best autistic life.

The ASD Grief Cycle

When we lose a loved one, we often hear about the grief cycle, which includes denial, anger, bargaining, depression, and acceptance. Some may argue that there are other stages, and while an autistic diagnosis does not bring on grief in the same way that it is brought on by a death—there can be grief uniquely associated with the identification of autism.

Shock and Disbelief

Receiving any news that may be perceived as bad can induce a knee-jerk reaction of shock and/or disbelief. Even if there has been an ongoing suspicion that there might be "something wrong" with your child, your attitude may be to question whether the diagnosis is correct. A symptom of shock and disbelief is becoming totally distracted while the doctor is explaining the intricacies of what the diagnosis actually means. You may experience self-contained panic as thoughts fly around in your head, leaving you unable to take in and process the information being conveyed.

Allow yourself to react in the way that you do; you can always see the doctor again. When you leave, don't self-judge. Let your body dictate your reaction. Isolate for a while if you need to, or surround yourself with friends and family. When calm descends, you can book another appointment and go in prepared with a list of questions and a positive disposition. Remember that there is no wrong, incorrect, or bad reaction. Just like your autistic child, reactions are different, that's all.

I'd like to address the sibling of the neurodivergent child. After a particularly rage-filled and exhausting morning over not being able to locate a hairbrush. My own son has asked me, "Why can't she just be normal?" My son's question made me so sad. I was sad for myself because I loved both my children, but I often found myself feeling anger, loss, jealousy, frustration, and even contempt when dealing with some of the unexpected anger outbursts from my daughter. Now I felt sorrow, guilt, loss, sadness, and discouragement for my son. At seven years old, he knew his friend's siblings were not this rageful. The temperament, age, gender, personality, and birth order of siblings make a difference in how they experience life with a neurodivergent brother or sister. Neurotypical siblings can have struggles, particularly with anxiety, depression, and social difficulties, so they should receive education and support.

Parents are encouraged to change their attitudes and the examples they set. Research by Debra Lobato found that siblings describing their own experiences consistently mentioned their parents' reactions, acceptance, and adjustment as the most significant influences on their experience of having a brother or sister with a disability (Lobato, 1990). It is also important to note from Lobato's research that a mother's mental and physical health is probably the most important factor in predicting sibling adjustment, regardless of the presence of disability in the family.

Denial

Denial is a more measured reaction than shock and the immediate thought that a mistake has been made with the diagnosis. That is why denial takes a bit more time, but it can provide the opportunity to get second opinions, which is completely understandable. A good tip is to use your denial positively and gather as much information as you can. Often, we know that we are in denial, and it is necessary to ride it out; denial will fade or could possibly just disappear when you come across a sign, have a discussion, or read something that brings acceptance. If you are aware of the denial, talk to a therapist to figure out what is behind it. Ultimately, as parents, we have to do what is best for ourselves, our children, and the entire family. We cannot do that if our denial prevents us from seeking the services our children need and deserve. They will grow up, and in any good parent's heart, we know we want their lives to be happy, so if our denial is preventing their success, growth, or happiness, we need to figure it out.

Anger or Rage

If denial does not quite get you to acceptance, anger or rage are likely to become your main emotions. There is a jealousy element as you question why this has not happened to another family or another child. You may wonder why people with children whose parents are bad to have happy, healthy kids when your parenting is much more loving and nurturing. Your anger could be directed at your spouse, your autistic child, or their siblings. That is the nature of anger: It is easily misdirected and can become all-consuming to the point where you live in your own head and fail to notice how you are affecting people at whom you lash out. Many people see anger as a bad thing, and to a degree, it is. However, we have to allow ourselves to feel that anger, but we also need to control it and not let it hurt the people we love. A tip extracted from Cognitive Behavior Therapy is to write things down: your feelings, your mindset, and your manifestation of anger. Writing may help!

Confusion and Powerlessness

As the saying goes, knowledge is power, and in the early stages, you will know very little about autism.

What you do know is probably ill-informed by society's misinterpretations, so don't beat yourself up if you have misconceptions about autism being a disease or a mental disorder. The terminology will be new, but you will learn. Just be cautious about believing everything that you read or watch. Read academic studies or articles on well-established sites and ask lots of questions in order to alleviate confusion and take back power and control.

Depression

Powerlessness is one thing, but hopelessness is another. It is common for parents to make a premature decision to give up, thinking that they do not have the skills to parent an autistic child effectively. A parent can get consumed with thoughts of how the plan went wrong. The perfect family and white picket fence were the dreams, but now the family is strained, both financially and emotionally, carrying an unfair burden and feeling extreme despair. There is no easy fix for depression, but the very first step is to seek out a counselor, therapist, or psychologist. Also, you still need to live for yourself, so take time out to treat yourself and do the things that bring you enjoyment.

Acceptance or Not?

George Orwell, the British novelist, is quoted as having said, "Happiness can exist only in acceptance."

He is correct, and as human beings, we have faults, we do the wrong things, and we hurt others. Sometimes we do so on purpose, and other times by mistake. Either way, we need to accept our faults, acknowledge our mistakes, and feel the associated emotions before moving forward. Acceptance of a diagnosis of autism is no different, but we also have to accept the reality that happiness is never permanent. There are bumps along the road; when the diagnosis is received, things will get tough. However, there will be wonderful, exciting, fun, and happy times too. Accepting the diagnosis leads to understanding and presents an opportunity to educate others, work on yourself as a parent, and tailor your parenting to cater to and support your autistic child without neglecting other loved ones. Look at acceptance as a call to action, which includes finding answers and creating empowerment in supporting your child.

What to Remember

You have your child's diagnosis, and you are experiencing this whirlwind of emotions, but what do you actually do with the diagnosis and all the collateral that it brings? The answer involves thought and action. Here are five quick tips for the effective, positive forward motion:

- Take a deep breath.

- Don't ever think that you are alone.

- Educate yourself on ASD and treatment options.

- Practice acceptance.

- Remember to connect with others who are in similar situations via groups, social media, etc.

What Does It Mean for Your Family?

You may have a spouse or partner and two children. Perhaps one of your children is autistic, and the other is not. You don't want either of your children to feel as though they are not getting enough love or attention. However, just like autism means differences, there are general differences between children in age, gender, interests, and emotions. No two children are the same, and no two children require exactly the same support. Having said that, supporting an autistic child can be time-consuming, to the point where your other child or even spouse feels left out or that you, as a parent or spouse, don't care as much. Communication is absolutely vital, and if your family can sit down every single evening and discuss the day with absolute honesty, then feelings of equal treatment, love, and support can be maintained. Communication! Communication! Communication!

Isolation and Special Treatment

Nobody enjoys the feeling of isolation, and you don't want anyone that you love to experience it. It can be tricky with one neurodivergent child and one neurotypical child, which is why everyone needs to feel equal involvement. Parents living their whole lives for their autistic children is common, and there is a tendency to be overprotective. In such cases, it may be your neurotypical child who experiences it. Spouses can also become isolated from each other due to feelings of distance created by not feeding the spousal relationship adequately. Your identity should not be as a family with an autistic child but rather as a family whose children have different needs and different support requirements. Also, remember that siblings argue, and even have physical fights, and sometimes it is just about growing up. You don't want to instill in your neurotypical-minded child that he or she cannot get angry with your autistic child or, on the other end, cannot tease sarcastically, for example. Shielding a young autistic person from real life is an easy thing to do, but life is not an easy gambit, and it is the job of parents, but also educators, to allow all children to experience life.

Children need to learn right from wrong. To take a small example, if you borrow something, you should return it in the same condition in which you received it. This is highly hypothetical, but let's say one of your children borrows a book from the other. When your child returns the book, there is a coffee stain on the cover, which wasn't there before. Obviously, it was a mistake, and you need to let your child, whether autistic or neurotypical, get upset with your other child. You can't prevent a confrontation because one of the two children is autistic. These are the types of learning experiences that children and young teens go through. As long as both children feel equally treated, you have achieved your goal, and as I said before, communication is vital, so if your children feel unequally treated, you need to discuss it as a family.

It also comes down to special treatment, which is essentially an isolation-creating endeavor in any case. Treatment must be different, not special; take small things like turns washing the dishes. You don't want to be saying, "Shame, he/she is autistic, so let's let him/her off on the chores."

That is special treatment. Parenting is a rocky road, but maintaining fairness and equal treatment, but by different means, is the best way to approach it.

Pay Attention to Other Stories

Never forget that you are not the first parent or family to have an autistic member, and there are many people with stories to tell. Talking and exchanging experiences can be empowering, which is why meeting with people who have autistic stories is a great way to feel heard and to give the courtesy of listening. What follows are explanations of two pieces of writing by Emily Perl Kingsley and Susan Rsuzidlo, fully referenced in the references section. They are interrelated as well as informative, but like anything, they have both garnered criticism, and rightly so.

Welcome to Holland ©

Some call it a poem; others call it an essay. Whichever category you put it in, Welcome to Holland © is Emily Perl Kingsley's take on not getting what you expected. She wrote the piece in 1987, and the message was a response to being frequently asked what it is like to raise a child with a disability. I mentioned 1987 for a reason, and that is because terms like "special needs" or "disability" have become outdated. In fact, Kingsley doesn't initially specify a diagnosis or condition but rather that her child has a disability before she begins to answer the question.

She talks about how the preparation for and excitement of having a baby are like preparing for and getting excited about a trip to Italy for an amazing holiday. However, when you touch down, you realize that you are actually in Holland, as the planning goes out the window and the disappointment descends. Kingsley goes on to suggest that, as calm sets in, the realization is that Holland is still a beautiful place. However, all the guidebooks, maps, and dictionaries for Italy have to be discarded. Then comes the challenge of acquainting yourself with new books, maps, and dictionaries. Basically, discarding what you had educated yourself on and planned for and learning something completely new.

Kingsley ends the novel in a heartbreaking way that may evoke thoughts of insensitivity and lack of acceptance. She talks about all the other people that successfully got to Italy and the stories that they tell when they return home. That was supposed to be the plan, but the pain of never having arrived never goes away. The last line is particularly poignant, and I will quote directly (Kingsley, E.P., 1987):

"But… if you spend your life mourning the fact that you didn't get to Italy, you may never be free to enjoy the very special, the very lovely things… about Holland."

A point that I have not yet mentioned is that Kingsley's son, the subject of her poem-turned-story, was born with Down syndrome thirteen years prior to its publication.

In a time of rife speculation, one could argue that Kingsley sees having a child with Down syndrome as missing out on something. I cannot say for sure, but if this is the case, then it is understandable that her piece of writing would leave many parents of children with Down syndrome very sad. It is a bit confusing, considering that Kingsley is a winner of multiple awards in media as well as Woman of the Year in 1983 in recognition of her volunteer activities. She has definitely done some excellent work, but her metaphor doesn't sit well. This can be applied to having an autistic child, but again, it doesn't seem very kind. Perhaps one can blame the times, but that shouldn't be the case.

Welcome to Beirut ©

Although this piece, often called a Parody, was penned in 1996, at that time, offensive and unkind words were still in mainstream use. Susan Rzucidlo is a naturopathic physician and author who has an autistic son. Some find her work inspiring, but as with Emily Perl Kingsley's, Welcome to Holland, criticism has been leveled.

The piece of writing is humorous in some parts, and Rzucidlo starts off by referring to a situation where parents or a parent are content with life. They have two children, one of whom is different, as is the case with siblings. She then describes the "terrorist kidnapping scene," often aired in popular media. The bag over the head kicks in the stomach, getting driven somewhere mysterious. She likes the experience of the day on which parents receive the diagnosis stating that their child is autistic.

Beirut is, of course, a war zone, and Rzucidlo uses bombs and bullets as metaphors for the terms that one starts to hear post-diagnosis. "Lifelong," "neurologically impaired," "refrigerator mother," "a good smack is all he needs." Next comes the freakout, especially because nothing has changed except a label. It sounds strange to say, "My child is autistic." You have zero knowledge of autism, and you don't know what to do. Being a lab rat is likened to case workers being assigned; although it is interesting that Rzucidlo refers to herself as the lab rat, the thinking is understandable.

She goes on, saying that you get hit by bombs, and this is where she starts getting kinder, with the example of her child being bullied and the heartache that it causes. The exclusion and isolation, not only of an autistic child but also of the parents, is the next topic, as are medical insurance companies that only care about money. We all know that, though.

Then Rzucidlo abandons the war zone idea and talks of the kindness that other people show. It is out there, like a neurotypical sticking up for an autistic child on the playground. Maybe an educator, a therapist, or a friend empathizes and explains the sensory overload that can be experienced. When your autistic child struggles in a social setting and displays attention-drawing behavior, someone offers a kind smile with an unspoken assurance that they understand. She quickly reverts back to the war, saying that it is awful, but there are lulls in the bombs and bullets. However, she signs off in a caring way, talking about how amazing the good times are. Her last two sentences make visceral sense, as she writes, "Life is good, but your life is never normal. Hey, what fun is normal."

The Message

This book is not about criticism; it is about awareness, changing views, recognizing differences, supporting needs, kindness, hope, and love. It is understandable that there may be sections of Welcome to Holland and Welcome to Beirut that seem objectionable. Metaphors are a good way to explain things, though. My advice is to understand the lessons and takeaway points that the metaphors illustrate. Discard the negativity, hold on to the positivity, and create an environment that promotes equal treatment for your loved ones. Equal does not mean identical; different approaches promoting equality of outcomes are what you are aiming for.

Chapter 7

Mindset Is Vital

If you go into a tennis match, to use an arbitrary example, and your mindset is that you are going to lose, you are halfway to that loss before you step onto the court. By way of another example, if you start learning the piano and your mindset is that you will never be good, then you are giving up before even giving yourself a chance. The same applies to your thought patterns and your focus on the positive rather than the negative. As I mentioned earlier, no person in the history of the world has walked through life without a single thing going wrong. On the days when things go wrong, and you feel like breaking down, just remember to get back to the correct mindset. A breakdown is fine as long as you acknowledge it, pick yourself up, and keep going. Stress is a reality, but it is an emotion or set of emotions that can be accentuated when raising autistic children.

Take It Day by Day

A commonly uttered phrase and a difficult mantra to live by, let alone implement. I don't mean that you shouldn't plan; planning is important, but know that the general plan will change from day to day. Children are people, just like adults, and they have different quirks. Teenagers can be disrespectful, autistic, or not. You don't know when your teenager is going to get argumentative and slam their door, but you know that it is bound to happen. On the day that it does, you already know how to deal with it; you were just not aware that it would happen on X-, Y-, or Z-day.

Learn to Manage, and Cater To Your Autistic Child's Differences

In any functional family, bearing in mind that the word "functional" could have many meanings, all members want to get to know each other well. If we know what our partner struggles with emotionally, we can be there for that person. Awareness is important, and as parents, you need to study your children. Not as in a scientific study but through observation, talking, and even trial and error exercises. Hypothetically, your autistic child is particularly sensitive to sound, more so than other sensory experiences. As a parent, you are aware of this, meaning that you can mitigate the discomfort, stress, and anxiety that your child feels by encouraging them to use noise-canceling headphones for argument's sake.

Prior to diagnosis, you may have been in a position of ignorance about the spectrum, neurodivergents, and neurotypicals. When you get the diagnosis, the learning must begin, both about your child and about autism in general. Knowledge is power, and with knowledge comes action.

Autism Management and Teaching Self-Care

If we look purely at statistics from the 2017 study by Shenoy, MD. et al, entitled Comprehensive Management of Autism: Current Evidence, it appears that nutrition and traditional medicine have a 74% prevalence rate in autistic children (Shenoy et al., 2017).

Intensive behavioral therapy and educational therapy, from as early an age as possible, have proved effective in allowing for better sensory experiences, or at the very least, the management thereof. These terms may seem a bit scientific, but all they represent is the implementation of measures to best support your autistic child. Things like role-play exercises involving your autistic child in activities that acclimate him or her to managing stressors. Encouraging social interactions, coaching how to handle them, and basically doing everything you can to give your autistic child the tools to have the best quality of life possible.

Self-care is very important, and as autistic children reach their teens, hygiene habits may change. A list of morning routines is very useful in helping your autistic child do the basics. Brush teeth, use the bathroom, shower, dry off, brush hair, use deodorant, put on clean underwear, and head downstairs for breakfast. As before, autistic children and adults, for that matter, like routines and having the instructions on the back of the bathroom door or stuck to the mirror is a small thing that goes an incredibly long way to promoting self-care.

As a parent, you also need to care for yourself; hygiene, yes, but as an adult, you probably have that covered. Parenting is tiring; nobody would argue against that, so take time for yourself when you can. Allow yourself a break, but also have fun with your kids. Slow down when you can; go for a walk in nature, read a book, do the things you love, de-stress, take a deep breath, and put your mom or dad hat back on for the next parenting whirlwind.

Adjusting Your Own Limitations

The sky's the limit, as we hear so often, but as educators and parents, we need to take a more practical approach and refer to the Welcome to Holland and Welcome to Beirut pieces from the previous chapter. Both had a sense of feeling inadequate, not having faith that they could parent effectively, and basically imposing limitations before taking action.

On the other side of the coin, there are imitations that you just cannot get around. No person can jump over a house, and we take that as a given. In other words, a limitation that is completely unchangeable. There is no point in even trying. To go back to self-care as an example, your autistic child may forget to put deodorant on, but that is something that can be fixed by reminders or a list on the mirror. As a parent, you are not limited in that sense. The adjustment comes in when things get a bit more complicated, and it comes down to control. You can supervise, help, and prepare, but you cannot know completely what is going to happen during your child's day.

In the same breath, as a non-therapist parent, you do not have the same knowledge and education that your child's therapist does. It may sound a bit harsh to classify this as a limitation but look at it in the sense of a physical wound. Your child cuts his or her arm; you clean the wound, apply pressure, bandage it up, and do what you can to the limits of your ability. Then you take your child to the hospital to get stitches. The same applies to caring for and feeding your autistic child's needs, to which there is a limit. For these reasons, therapy and tailored education are so important.

Coping With Negative Emotions

Negative emotions impact all of us, but some people manage them better than others. Many neurodiverse individuals cope with emotions better than neurotypicals, and emotional management is important not only for your child but for yourself as a parent. Identifying the source is the first step towards either eliminating the emotion or anticipating it in order to brace for it.

Let's look at resentment via a realistic scenario. As a parent of an autistic child, there is the real possibility of not being invited to social events due to the perception that your child is badly behaved or attention-seeking. The resulting resentment could be directed at your friends who do not invite you over anymore. Don't ignore the emotion; rather, track the source, or the cause, which is essentially the fact that your friends don't know anything about autism. Yes, there is an element of avoiding unpleasantness on their part, as in not inviting you in case your child becomes overwhelmed for whatever reason and has a panic attack. That is not your fault at all, but you also have to understand their position. From there, the best way is to talk; explain to them what autism is, what it means, and how your autistic child faces challenges that he or she deals with differently than neurotypicals.

The above sounds like a very easy method to apply, but it isn't. There are so many variables. Maybe your friends don't want to talk, or even if they do, their minds won't be changed. Perhaps they don't care about the reasons behind your child's actions in a way that they erroneously see as abnormal. You need to deal with emotions on a situational basis. Later in this chapter is a section on mindfulness, which will be very useful in learning emotion management tools.

While on the topic of resentment, you can't be blind to the possibility that you may feel resentment towards your autistic child for making your life and the lives of your family difficult or unpleasant. Feeling this type of resentment can then prompt guilt, followed by turning the resentment on yourself, and it is not unusual for depression to set in. Once again, you need to identify the source or cause. That little person is not at fault in any way at all, so the feeling is unfounded, but it is still present. If you acknowledge the above, then you can rationalize what is rational and begin to let go of the resentment.

In general, the human race is inherently negative, so coping can be incredibly difficult, whatever your circumstance or position in life. It is a step-by-step, day-by-day process that requires continuous work.

Understanding Your Child's Stressors

Like everyone else, autistic children experience positive and negative emotions. Just as a parent needs to identify the cause of their own emotions in order to manage them, that parent also needs to identify the causes of their autistic child's emotions, otherwise known as stressors.

We know that sensory experiences can be unpleasant and that a flickering light, a shirt label, or being overloaded by anxiety or panic-creating noises are stressors, but understanding them on a deeper level can help us to help our autistic children more effectively.

No Finite Set of Rules

As we know, autistic individuals like routines and going about daily tasks via a set of finite rules. An unexpected change in routine can be a major stressor. In a logical sense, a bus delay will cause stress to neurotypicals, so why should it not do the same to neurodiverse people? A person canceling a coffee meeting at the last minute can be a cause of irritation and stress, no matter who you are, but in autism, the stress manifests differently. Rules and schedules are often broken as nobody's fault, and it is the unpredictability that can be troubling. As a neurotypical parent, it is easy to understand from personal experiences that changes in plans cause stress. From that point, it becomes easier to understand the same stressor as experienced by autistic individuals.

Sensory Processing

As we know, autistic individuals process sensory information differently. However, if you compare yourself, as a neurotypical parent, to your autistic child, you will realize that your experiences are not "that" different. A flashlight being shined in your eye is going to cause distress; that is what it is like for an autistic child in what one may term a "normal light setting." The same principle is there for noises: If someone claps really loudly, right next to your ear, it is going to be unpleasant and stress- or anxiety-inducing. Your autistic child feels the same, but the clap is soft. So, in terms of sensory processing, you kind of start with the result, then move back to the cause, which is pretty much the same in autistic and neurotypical individuals. One could refer to it as the intensity of the sensory experience.

Social Situations

Although social interactions can be uncomfortable for neurodivergents, they can also be uncomfortable for neurotypicals. Similarly, to sensory processing, it is the intensity of the experience that marks the difference. In life, you get incredibly social individuals that will go to the park and ask to join a game of catch or touch football. For others, just the thought is a dreadful prospect. Social interactions are a double whammy, considering that sensory exposure also plays a part. You will remember the social stressor sections at the end of chapter three and the beginning of chapter four. When you understand the nature of the stressors, you can implement exercises, role-play, and home education.

Signs That Indicate the Existence of Stressors

The more you understand your autistic child and autism in general, the easier it becomes to identify when a stressor is being experienced or is approaching. You can then remove your child from that situation, and when he or she regains composure, you can give them praise.

- A few examples of stressor indicators are:

- Uncomfortable hand movements

- Swaying back and forth

- Generally distressed demeanor

- Looking down

- Pacing or walking in circles

How Do Your Child's Stressors Affect You?

Because we love our children, we often feel their emotions along with them. Stress from any source can be debilitating, and constant worry about your autistic child is a source of stress. When you leave the house, you will probably be concerned that your child will encounter a stressor and have a breakdown. If you are at home and your child is out playing, you are likely to fear bullying, sensory stressors, or adverse reactions that others may not know how to deal with.

Unfortunately, statistics do show that 50% of mothers express a decreased enjoyment of life due to the stress of managing their family, including their autistic child (Boyd, 2002). Mothers and fathers provide support for their children and for each other. However, in order to be in the other 50%, support is needed from an outside source, such as a therapist or a therapy group.

Stress Management for Yourself

You need to be kind to yourself. Remember that exercise is a great stress reliever, largely because of the dopamine release. Also, if you are really exercising hard, you can't think deeply or over-analyze. Deep breathing and guided meditation are great sources of stress relief and fall under mindfulness, which I will get to shortly. Keeping a diary is an excellent way to de-stress. Go old school and write down your thoughts and feelings in an exercise book, not in a document on your computer. Personally, you might not be an "exerciser," or you may not enjoy writing; maybe you like swimming in the sea or reading fantasy novels. Do what works for you!

Mindfulness

You may have heard of Cognitive Behavioral Therapy (CBT), from which mindfulness is derived. They are not the same thing, but they do overlap and can be tremendously helpful in dealing with your emotions as a parent. Mindfulness techniques have been shown to be useful as part of therapy for autistic children. A semi-branch off is called Dialectic Behavioral Therapy (DBT). I am not going to go into the science and origins but rather explain how to apply a mixture of all three.

Parents/Adults

The first step is to acknowledge your emotions, which can be difficult. It is common to suppress our emotions or even ignore them. This leaves open the possibility of exploding one day and taking it out on others. The difficulties that you are having in your role as a parent can create frustration, anger, anxiety, stress, resentment, or a combination thereof. A good way to explain the next step is to describe it as an out-of-body experience, not in any supernatural way, but rather as a figurative backward step that allows you to look at your feelings and emotions in an objective way. I could compare it to standing directly in front of a painting. Everything is blurred, and you can't discern one color or depiction from the others. Take a few steps back, and the painting becomes clearer.

It is important to recognize where your anger came from, for instance. Perhaps you have been feeling that your partner has not been contributing equally to the household, emotionally or otherwise. You might start to feel bad because you haven't raised the issue, but that is okay. Now you need to remove self-judgment, which is a tough thing to do. Looking from a vantage point, you are allowed to forgive yourself. You then put yourself in a position to address the root cause. We do tend to catastrophize and think of the worst, but a simple discussion may reveal that your spouse or partner has been mentally distracted by a particular ongoing stressful work scenario. The next step is easy, sort of; you need to have a discussion and learn from the experience, which means you will know what to do the next time.

Another tenet of the trifecta is being acutely aware of your surroundings as you employ your senses to really focus on the seemingly mundane. This part of the technique acts as a distraction from the stress you may be carrying. Often, we rush around in the mornings: In and out of the shower, a quick brush of the teeth, getting changed in a hurry, whipping up a quick breakfast, and heading out the door. The sequence is not a stressor as such, but it does cause unnecessary stress and anxiety that can compound the longer-term emotions that we feel. Give yourself an extra half hour and take everything in— really feel the warm droplets in the shower. Pay attention to how they run down your back. Take time to enjoy the feeling; observe the texture of your toothbrush, and think of how amazing it is that we humans even have teeth. Pick out your clothes slowly, think how lucky you are to be able to eat breakfast, and use that thought to observe the different tastes. These types of deep observations can be applied all day. The name of the game is being present, which has great and holistic mental health benefits.

Guided meditation is similar, but it directs focus to your body as you lie down or sit in a comfortable chair with your eyes closed. Guided meditation can be combined with deep breathing, the observation of your chest moving up and down, your lungs filling with air, the slow release, and the calm that should descend. You can be attentive to your toes, wiggle them around, feel the sensations, and aim to be completely present. Thoughts will definitely pop into your head, but make it your goal to let them go and reset your focus. Ten minutes, three times a week, and you will improve your "being present" skills.

Children

The same general idea of mindfulness applies to autistic children, but it is much harder to embrace what is essentially something very different. Children might find it silly at first, but a slow introduction and continued mindfulness practice have shown to garner excellent results in understanding and managing stressors and reactions thereto. There is room for adaptability, and also for the parent or educator to become the guide where applicable.

Here are a few exercises to test out:

Sound Meditation

You can get creative with this one. Ask your child to lie down or sit comfortably and make a sound. Even a spoon tapping on a glass will work. Start from a distance and tap a few times very quietly, then ask your child to describe the sound and the reaction. Move a bit closer, and repeat. Practicing this regularly can help with the management of the overwhelm that may be felt. When one gets used to something, it becomes somewhat innocuous. Your end goal is to create a few different sounds to show your child that they are capable of managing audible sensory experiences.

Guided Meditation/Relaxation

Exactly the same as the parent version, but for short stints, followed by reports about the experience.

Conscious Breathing

Technically, you can't see yourself breathing, but you can do exercises like holding a tissue close to your child's mouth and asking them to observe the motion of the tissue as they breathe out, followed by the calming motion as they breathe in. Benefits include improved hand-eye coordination, motor skills, and fun!

Mindful Walking

Go on observational walks with your autistic child. Encourage him or her to look at the colors of the trees and flowers, listen to the birds chirping, take in the smells, and report back. Implementation of your own mindful morning routine can also be taught, within the rules that your child observes, of course.

Staying in Control

Children can be manipulative, and they will pounce on any opportunity to take control away from their parents. However, as long as your child or children know that you are in charge, parenting is ever so slightly easier.

Adapting to New Routines and Using Schedules

Routine is good for children, whether they are neurodiverse or neurotypical, but the latter are better at adapting to new routines. It is a good idea to mix up routines, even if the adjustment is slight. Getting a whiteboard with markers and writing out a daily schedule is a great exercise. Perhaps you and your child would like to plan a two-day schedule and write it on the whiteboard together. Well, in advance of day two, you can introduce a very small change. For instance, if your family takes a mindful walk at 4 p.m. every day, move it to 4.30 p.m., and after dinner on the evening of day one, explain that the routine on day two will change. Rub out the 4 p.m. walk and replace it with the 4.30 p.m. walk. This is slow preparation for bigger changes, such as taking on a new type of therapy or going on an unplanned trip to the beach. Try to keep last-minute schedule changes to a minimum. Autistic children like a plan, so introduce small adjustments as a start.

Reward Good Behavior and Build Self-Esteem

Use positive praise to reinforce attempts, not results: "You worked really hard on that" or "You were able to figure that out even though it was difficult." If we can accept that we are insufficient in certain areas but still choose to like ourselves, then we are developing self-esteem. Successful interactions in terms of words, used positively, allow autistic children to grow their self-esteem. It is important to build a child's belief that they can handle their life and handle it well.

Make Your Home a Safety Zone

You don't want to have blinding lights or ranges of powerful colors, nor an environment that is too busy. Dim but pleasant lighting and the use of natural light where possible augur well for a comfortable and safe environment, which should be the case at home. The same applies to sound: Have the TV at a reasonable level, tell your child when you are going to fire up the washing machine, and allow some distance from the sound. Specify that homework must be done at table X and that eating must be done at the Y table. Keep pens, pencils, glue sticks, scissors, and other homework tools in the same place, preferably labeled. Keep dangerous items, like sharp knives, out of reach. Do the same with cleaning products that contain chemicals and with anything else that may cause harm. This is quite a logical one. Teach stranger danger and stress that your child, autistic or otherwise, must not open the door for someone they don't know. Rather be safe than sorry on all of the above aspects.

Nonverbal Observation

As we get to know someone better, we learn what a certain look means, what a gesture is telling us, what their eyes are saying, or how a nod is a signal for something.

Facial Expressions and Gestures of Autistic Children

As a parent or educator, you need to identify gestures and facial expressions that a child may use to indicate tiredness, hunger, or discomfort. Achieving this shouldn't be too hard, considering that parents generally get to know their child from birth and through the different stages thereafter.

Identifying Reasons for Tantrums

Obviously, a tantrum is not a silent occurrence, but it doesn't involve cogent verbal communication. Just like expressions and gestures, parents of autistic children will learn why their child has tantrums. Don't think for one second that neurotypical children don't have tantrums, but do think that the reasons may be different.

Pay Attention to Sensory Activities

As a parent, you will know how your child reacts, maybe scrunching up their eyes, covering their ears, or fiddling with their hands. It is more than just knowing how your child reacts; you need to be continuously observant, especially when entering an environment that may cause sensory overload.

Living in the Present

Mindset is vital; let me repeat! You will have to make adjustments and adaptations. You will have stress, and there will be tough times. However, you have the ability to be as kind to yourself as you are to your autistic child. Practice mindfulness, and teach mindfulness to your child or children. Plan a few days ahead in terms of scheduling, but learn to live in the present.

Chapter 8

The Future Is Possible

The title of the previous chapter and the final sign-off paragraph are "living in the present." If we leave the past behind and live in the present, then the future is most certainly possible.

Unique Personalities in General

We can draw comparisons and extract similarities in personality or personality type, but no two personalities are the same. Opposites do attract, as they say, and sometimes they do, but often you and your best friend have incredibly similar traits that you express through your quirks. We tend to group types of people together, but groups overlap, and the wonderful thing is that we do not need to fit into a specific group.

Unique Personalities Specific to Autistic Individuals

Some people may dismiss autistic people as all being the same, and it does happen. As a parent of an autistic child, you will know that this is a ridiculous assertion. That is akin to saying that all asthmatics are the same or that all diabetics are the same. Similar traits exist but think about our associations and friendships. Take reading, for instance. You may be part of a book club, and that is the common interest, so you identify with the other members. However, you don't all need to like the same books. A good way to look at it is in a very broad sense, and I will continue with the book club example. Millions upon millions of people enjoy reading, but a smaller group prefers nonfiction; within nonfiction, some like self-help, others like biographies; you get the picture.

Autistic individuals tend to show signs of introversion, but so does half the world; thus, introversion is a broad category, but within introversion, you get different types of introverts. It could be argued that autistic individuals show more similarities than differences, but that is very debatable, and even if that is the case, it doesn't matter.

Anxiety Prone

To label autistic individuals as more likely to experience anxiety is not really putting those individuals in a box because it is the neurological part that conjures the similarity. People that have depression or PTSD, for instance, are prone to anxiety, and bearing in mind that sensory experiences bring on anxiety in autistic children, anxiety is not a personality trait, just like depression is not a personality trait.

Perceived Social Aloofness

Social aloofness is perhaps slightly closer to being a personality trait, but I am cautious about putting it in that category, largely because it is a neurotypical perception that is most often wrong. It is not a case of being disinterested in interacting socially, as opposed to the difficulty of overcoming the stress involved. In life, some people are just aloof and think that they are too good for the rest of us—a trait indeed of a narcissist. The big difference is that aloofness is part of a narcissistic personality, whereas an autistic individual is mistaken for being aloof by others.

Persistence

Being persistent is probably the closest aspect of a personality representation. To bring ADHD, a common trait is the inability to finish tasks or the abandonment of tasks when the person does not know what to do. Autistic children experience frustration differently, but not that differently. A neurotypical can be prone to getting frustrated and stressed out by failing to do something that doesn't appear difficult. Trying to learn how to play the piano is difficult, and people with low patience will undoubtedly struggle. Is low patience a personality trait, though? I'm reluctant to answer my own question because a lack of patience may be reframed as a problem with persistence.

The Personality Trait Model

Referred to as the "Big Five" personality trait model, this categorization of personality traits is most definitely a refined model compared with historical models. If we go back to the early twentieth century, there was a psychologist by the name of Gordon Allport who created a model defining 4504 different personality traits (Cherry, 2020).

Jump forward to 1947 and a book called Dimensions of Personality, written by Hans Eysenck, which theorizes that there are two dimensions: extraversion and neuroticism. In the late 1970s, he added psychoticism to complete the trifecta (Team, 2011). In more modern times, extensive research has produced what is widely recognized as the foremost model, i.e., the Big Five (Cherry, 2020).

Each part of the model is broken down into "high" and "low." The former means that a particular person is at the top of the scale in terms of emotion, whereas the latter refers to someone near the bottom.

Openness

A broad range of interests and inquisitiveness about other people, places, and things fall into the high category. On the low end, the hypothetical person is averse to change, lacks imagination, and is unlikely to want to step outside their comfort zone.

Conscientiousness

The highly conscientious individual is very attentive to the smallest of details, likes to have a set plan and/or schedule, and attends to important tasks first and, most often, immediately. At the bottom is the type of person who procrastinates, struggles to complete tasks, can't stick to schedules, behaves recklessly, and does not look after things.

Extraversion

As we probably already know, an extrovert is very open to meeting new people, striking up conversations with strangers, and maintaining high energy levels, often feeding off the energy of others. This type of person will generally have a large group of friends and will enjoy being the center of attention. It goes without saying that an extrovert is on the high side of this category. At the bottom of the scale is, of course, the introvert, who does not crave attention, is happier on their own, and finds socializing exhausting.

Agreeableness

On the plus side, we find people who display kindness and have a genuine interest in helping others that require assistance. Often, these attributes are accompanied by empathy and concern. The low part here is the kind of person that you want to avoid. They don't care about others, are quick to throw out insults, and are particularly skilled in manipulation.

Neuroticism

At the top end, people get upset quite easily. They display high levels of stress and find it difficult to recover quickly from a particularly stressful event. Anxiety and excessive worry tend to be present, which lend themselves to fast changes in mood. Being low in terms of this trait involves the ability to relax easily, dispel worrisome events, and get over setbacks very quickly.

What Now?

Understanding these personality traits can assist us in identifying the parts of our personalities that we don't like and wish to change. The same applies to helping your autistic child do the same thing. There are positives and negatives to each of the Big Five, depending on whether you fit into the low or high category according to each trait.

Some of the positives:

• Being respectful

• Displaying friendly behavior

• Considering the feelings of others before acting

• Showing humility

• Cooperating as opposed to seeking out conflict or argument

• Always exercising objectivity

Some of the negatives:

• Intolerance towards others and dismissive of their opinions

- Selfishness

- Being overly judgmental, especially when you display the same characteristics

- Lacking reliability

- Openly behaving in an arrogant manner

Self-Insight

The American Psychological Association (APA), Dictionary of Psychology, defines self-insight as:

"Understanding oneself in some depth—it is the mediate goal or the desired outcome of many types of psychotherapy."

Like parts of one's disposition or personality, self-insight needs to be worked on. It is hard enough to accept ourselves as we are, let alone gain a deep understanding of ourselves.

Self-Insight vs. Self-Awareness

Self-insight is the "why," and self-awareness is the "what" and the "how." The former refers to understanding why you act in the way that you do and why you think in the manner that you do. Furthermore, self-insight dictates whether or not one must continue acting and thinking in certain ways or whether changes need to be implemented. The latter knows what you do, and how you think and the effect that these actions and thoughts have on others.

The Theory of Mind

The theory deals with understanding the minds of others, what is going on in their heads, and essentially what they are thinking. We obviously learn more about the way people act, react, and display feelings as we get to know them better. One could term it observational, but it is also automatic in a sense, given that the ability to understand actions, reactions, and feelings starts developing in children around the age of three.

In autistic children, the theory of mind is not as clear-cut as it is in neurotypicals. In 1984 and 1985, a British clinical psychologist by the name of Simon Baron-Cohen, with the help of German psychologist Uta Frith and Scottish psychologist Alan Leslie, came up with the false belief test, also called the Sally/Anne test. The premise is that a young girl puts a ball in a basket and goes out for a walk; her name is Sally. Another young girl by the name of Anne then takes the ball out of the basket and places it in a box before Sally returns from her walk. This is a simple scenario. However, many autistic children, when asked where Sally will "look" for the ball, answer that she will look in the box. It is important to remember that the question deals with looking, not finding. The more likely scenario is that Sally would look in the basket because that is where she left the ball, but that would be a false belief because she does not know that the ball has been moved. Autistic children struggle to identify that false belief.

In their studies and administration of the test, the three psychologists found that 20% of autistic children could identify the false belief, while the other 80% could not. The results are fascinating, but their simplicity tells us a lot about the perceived differences in autistic children.

Deficit

First of all, we should not be using the word "deficit" because something is not missing in the cognition of autistic children. One observation is that autistic individuals find that understanding or identifying figurative speech is quite difficult. Let's say, for instance, an autistic child stands on a sharp rock and cuts themselves. These things hurt, but when asked how they feel, through tears or clenched teeth, the answer may be that they are happy. It is a case of not being in touch with feelings and giving an answer that they feel is correct. The same may apply when they witness another child, a neurotypical, let's say, succumb to a cut from the rock. A present lack of understanding is at play, which is why the term "deficit" seems to have stuck.

Another difficulty comes into play when reading fiction. Generally, autistic individuals prefer facts, and exploring facts lends itself to answering the "why" question. In any event, children love that question. In a fictional book, one character may play a practical joke on another, and the autistic reader may wonder why Brian and Sue, hypothetically, were involved. This goes back to the chicken crossing the road joke and the literal manner in which an autistic child may interpret it before concluding that it is silly or nonsensical. A good exercise is to review real-life situations that your autistic child has encountered and guide them as to how they felt, followed by a lesson on why they felt that way. The idea is that the child will then be able to understand, or at the very least identify, what another person is thinking in a similar situation. As your child starts to answer the "why" question in his or her own mind, the so-called deficit evens out.

Impairment in Social Interaction

In terms of the theory of mind, the literal interpretation also goes to the heart of social interaction. The aloofness referred to earlier can present itself in social interactions when an autistic child just cannot understand a metaphor or the need for it. As before, routines are like a constant reassurance because the child knows what comes next, what comes after that, and so on. Social interaction sometimes comes without a plan. As an example, a bunch of kids agree to meet at the park on their bikes, then decide whether they will throw a ball around or play catch. This can be disconcerting for an autistic individual; he or she would prefer a specific plan, i.e., ride to the park, play catch, or ride home.

Impairment in Communication

Imagine if you knew what someone was talking about but found the conversation boring. In your own mind, you start thinking about what you would like to add to the discussion, and you read the verbal and nonverbal cues in order to choose the right time to speak. Autistic children often don't change topics tactfully and might just interrupt and move on to what they want to talk about. Interrupting is rude, but the autistic individual may not understand that because they struggle with interpreting what the other participant is thinking or even why they are talking about something so boring.

Restrictive Behavior

Within this category, we have repetition in a verbal and nonverbal sense. Repeating the same motions, sitting in the same chair, wearing the same clothes, and following the same general routine characterize behavior that can be restrictive. The same applies to eating only a few types of food, preferring very specific lighting, and repeating facts on their favorite topics. Stimming, as discussed previously, comes into play, in addition to hours of focus on one thing only. Their behaviors are not autism-specific; many neurotypicals display restrictive behavior, maybe not to the extent of their autistic peers, but it is still there.

Language Deficits

Many of us, probably all of us, sometimes forget mid-sentence what we are talking about or struggle to find the correct word, which is one of the reasons for using "ummm" and "like" to give us time to think. Autistic individuals experience this differently, and it can be a challenge to get the words out. Otherwise, there can be an overuse of words in the form of blurting out something that doesn't make cognitive sense. Some autistic children develop the ability to speak at an older age than others, and some have limited language their whole lives. Neither is bad nor wrong; they just indicate in what areas more support is required.

Becoming a Human of Value

A whole bunch of humans go through life believing that they bring no value to society, but one could argue that a huge proportion of them are wrong. People recover from alcoholism, drug addiction, or gambling to regain their human value. It happens all the time, and value is different from person to person. Teachers add value, as do nurses, but housewives also add value. If you can make someone's life better by showing kindness, doing a favor, or helping a friend, you are adding more value than you might think. It doesn't matter if you are autistic or not. You don't have to invent something amazing, become famous, or get really rich. As a parent of an autistic child, you need to spread love, and when you receive that love back, you will know for sure that your child is adding value. Seeing your child's progress will make you proud of yourself and of your child.

Always remember what Winnie the Pooh said to Piglet when Piglet asked Winnie how to spell love:

"You don't spell it. You feel it."

Spreading love, even if it is unspoken, is becoming a human value.

Conclusion

I am sure you will agree with me when I say that the last eight chapters have been quite a ride! As parents, educators, autistic children or adults, brothers, and sisters, plus anyone else who has read the book, I hope that you have learned something, perhaps many somethings! I also hope that I have been able to change perceptions and dispel erroneous beliefs about autism. What follows is a brief recap that you can use to consolidate what you have read and, if need be, refer back to certain sections.

The term "neurodiverse" is an indicator that our brains operate in diverse ways. There is, however, a distinction between neurodiverse and neurotypical individuals. Not only does the former describe diversity in brain activity, but it also encompasses a range of mental illnesses. Autism and ADHD are not mental illnesses, and neurodivergent individuals are not sick, disabled, or have special needs. Autistic children and adults experience the world differently, that's all. The old-fashioned and offensive terms, as well as general language, need to be reformulated. As an example from chapter one, a child is autistic, not autism.

Explaining to children at a young age that they are autistic is highly encouraged, and in such cases, it has been shown that the quality of life is better as young autistic children grow up. Interestingly, gender differences play a role in the identification of autism in that autistic boys are easier to identify than autistic girls. Sadly, the stigma stretches across gender lines, but ongoing research and awareness are slowly making a dent in that stigma.

Sensory experiences are central to differences in processing between autistic and neurotypical children. You will remember the analysis of the eight senses and the manner in which hearing, for example, is somewhat of an assault on the ears. Similarly, what one would consider being comfortable lighting may be near-blinding for an autistic child. Furthermore, the vestibular system establishes differences in spatial awareness, balance, and coordination. These sensory challenges can be overwhelming and can create extreme stress and discomfort. In general, sensory processing has been shown to be challenging for neurodivergent individuals.

Self-regulation, which involves stimulatory behavior, is a defense tactic. Parents and educators can assist in developing these combat tactics in order to improve quality of life.

A point of parental awareness must be directed towards masking or camouflaging, which entails autistic individuals developing a persona according to the way in which they think they should act. We want autistic children to be themselves and maintain a sense of individual identity. Masking and camouflaging contribute to the late identification of autism, which makes it more difficult to ease the need for autistic children to hide their true selves.

The neurodivergent development of social skills is different, and due to no fault of their own, autistic children can have trouble communicating. Rudeness is often an unfounded perception among neurotypicals. However, due to the literal nature of autistic children, manners may appear to be lacking. Initiating conversations, especially with strangers, may be daunting, and the stress involved often contributes to not participating at all; otherwise, people avoid eye contact, often unknowingly, and miss social cues.

Friendships appear difficult to form, but explanations and different exercises can ease the difficulty. An excellent way to slowly introduce autistic children into "friend-making scenarios" is through sports. Like-mindedness and enjoyment of the same activities can be a kick-start to discussions. Autistic children tend to prefer individual sports involving other participants. Examples would be swimming, horseback riding, and martial arts.

We often hear the term "constructive criticism," which doesn't apply exactly to autistic children, but using words and sentences in a constructive way is of great use. It can be challenging to understand how autistic individuals function, but with awareness of schedules, routines, and stressors, that understanding can be broadened. It also helps to take note of the levels of autism and the corresponding support requirements, in addition to the differences between the medical and social models. In a sentence, the former indicates a disease or problem, whereas the latter describes social differences, not abnormalities.

Sadly, autistic individuals have shown a propensity for self-harm, and one of the reasons is that depression and chronic anxiety can be coupled with autism. Life expectancy in autistic people is not very high, and a contentious issue is the lack of willingness shown by medical insurance companies to assist financially. This is something that we can work at changing by spreading awareness and giving the autistic community, their families, and advocates a platform to have their voices heard.

We do try to stray away from the term "diagnosis," but for the sake of practicality, receiving one can evoke a spectrum of feelings. Some parents experience fear, others feel relief or perhaps regret, and often need to progress through the ASD grief cycle to find acceptance. The Holland and Beirut stories may have assisted you in putting things into perspective and facilitated a way of understanding and explaining what it is like to receive the diagnosis and go on with life thereafter. Your mindset may require adjustment, and living day by day can make parenting a little easier. Negativity is bound to creep in, but alleviating the associated stress and anxiety should be achieved by being kind to yourself. Your autistic child may struggle with self-care and need reminders to brush his or her teeth. For instance, as a parent, you need to take care of yourself by doing things you enjoy.

Mindfulness is something to look into. It is rooted in being present, focusing on the now, and distracting yourself from the stressful thoughts that are firing around in your brain. Mindfulness can also improve the quality of life for autistic children, and it can be done together.

Don't lose sight of the fact that you are working towards a world in which autistic children can display their unique personalities. Make it your goal to prove the theory of mind wrong, or at least to give your autistic child the tools to remove perceived deficits, and restrictive behavior and become socially comfortable. Show your autistic child what it means to be a person of value, and learn the same thing from them using the most powerful human connection tool, love.

I would like to leave you, the reader, with a quote by the highly respected autism advocate Temple Grandin:

"Your autistic child has unlimited potential, just like everyone else."

Don't forget that, and don't let your child forget that either.

References

A CHAT WITH THE SPEECH THERAPIST

Agin, Marilyn C, et al. The Late Talker: What to Do If Your Child Isn't Talking Yet. New York, St. Martin's Press, 2004.

American Speech-Language-Hearing Association. (n.d.). Early
Intervention.
https://www.asha.org/public/speech/earlyintervention/

Ayala Manolson. It Takes Two to Talk: [a Parent's Guide to Helping Children Communicate]. Toronto, Hanen Centre, 1992.

Girolametto, Luigi, et al. Learning Language and Loving I Teacher Interaction and Language Rating Scale / Developed by Luigi Girolametto, Elaine Weitzman, and Janice Greenberg. Toronto, The Hanen Centre Cop, 2000.

Heller, Sharon. Too Loud, Too Bright, Too Fast, Too Tight: What to Do If You Are Sensory Defensive in an Overstimulating World. New York; London, Harper, 2003.

Marshalla, Pam. The Marshalla Guide: A Topical Anthology of Speech Movement Techniques for Motor

Speech

Disorders & Articulation Deficits. Ashland, Or, Marshalla Speech And Language, 2019.

Narayanan, K. (2021, October 18). High tech and low tech AAC: How to effectively use both. Avaz Inc. Retrieved April 14, 2023, from
https://www.avazapp.com/blog/high-tech-and-low-tech-aac how-to-effectively-use-both/

References

Give Them The Words

Alhujaili, N., Platt, E., Khalid-Khan, S., & Groll, D. (2022). Comparison of social media use among adolescents with autism spectrum disorder and non-ASD adolescents. Adolescent health, medicine and therapeutics, Volume 13, 15–21. https://doi.org/10.2147/ahmt.s344591

Atske, Sara. (2022, December 15). Teens and cyberbullying 2022. www.pewresearch.org/internet/2022/12/15/teens-and-cyberbullying-2022/

Beck, C. (2022, December 06). Understanding sensory dysregulation. https://www.theottoolbox.com/understanding-sensory-dysregulation/

Better health. (2014). Nervous system. Vic.gov.au. https://www.betterhealth.vic.gov.au/health/conditionsandtreatments/nervous-system

Brennan, D. (2021, October 25). What is echolalia? https://www.webmd.com/parenting/what-is-echolalia

Cherry, K. (2022, November 7). What is emotional intelligence? Verywell Mind. https://www.verywellmind.com/what-is-emotional-intelligence-2795423

Children & autism: Videos. (n.d.). Raising Children Network. Retrieved April 25, 2023, from http://raisingchildren.net.au/autism/children-autism-videos

Delano, C. (2021, July 28). Benefits of early intervention speech therapy. Autism Parenting Magazine. https://www.autismparentingmagazine.com/early-intervention-speech-therapy/

Delano, C. (2022, February 18). Benefits of sign language for autism. https://www.autismparentingmagazine.com/autistic-child-sign-language/

Echolalia and its role in gestalt language acquisition. (n.d.). American Speech-Language-Hearing Association. https://www.asha.org/Practice-Portal/Clinical-Topics/Autism/Echolalia-and-Its-Role-in-Gestalt-Language-Acquisition/

Gordon, S. (2022, November). What is hyperlexia? Verywell Family. https://www.verywellfamily.com/hyperlexia-signs-diagnosis-and-treatment-5206172

Gray, C. (2015). Social stories. Carol Gray - Social Stories. https://carolgraysocialstories.com/about-2/carol-gray/

Guidance, T. F., & Center, T. (2022, January 21). Do autistic people have emotional intelligence? Familyguidanceandtherapy.com. https://familyguidanceandtherapy.com/do-autistic-individuals-have-emotional-intelligence/

A guide to the individualized education program office

of special education and rehabilitative services U.S. department of education. (2000). https://www2.ed.gov/parents/needs/speced/iepguide/iepguide.pdf

Helping kids understand the connection between feelings and moods. (n.d.). Fit.sanfordhealth.org. https://fit.sanfordhealth.org/units/u2-k2-helping-kids-manage-feelings-and-emotions/u2l1-k2-helping-kids-understand-the-connection-between-feelings-and-moods

Home. (n.d.). Key Autism Services. http://www.keyautismservices.com

Home. (n.d.-b). Center for Autism and Related Disorders (CARD®). http://centerforautism.com

Hyperlexia: What is it, and how can I support a hyperlexic learner? (2023). Twinkl.com. http://www.twinkl.com/blog/hyperlexia-what-is-it-and-how-can-i-support-a-hyperlexic-learner

Kuypers, L. (2014, December). Emotional self regulation | senses. Scribd. https://www.scribd.com/doc/312176471/leah-kuypers-handouts-zones-of-regulation?utm_medium=cpc&utm_source=google_pmax&utm_campaign=3Q_Google_Performance-Max_RoW&utm_term=&utm_device=c&gclid=CjwKCAjw9J2iBhBPEiwAErwpeaE3qHq5WUEmZT-7WyFYFB_m2dYllJvuTh-FXu-zcFtK4OzWB2TF7BoCK8UQAvD_BwE#

Kuypers, L. (2011). The zones of regulation: A concept to foster self-regulation & emotional control. The Zones of Regulation. https://zonesofregulation.com/index.html

Joiya, S.. (2018, November 20). 5 steps to emotional intelligence. Autism Point. https://autismpoint.com/5-steps-to-emotional-intelligence/

Lovering, N. (2016, October 14). Autism and logical thinking: What to know. Psych Central. https://psychcentral.com/autism/why-people-with-autism-are-more-logical

Magnuson, K. M., & Constantino, J. N. (2011). Characterization of depression in children with autism spectrum disorders. Journal of Developmental & Behavioral Pediatrics, 32(4), 332–340. https://doi.org/10.1097/dbp.0b013e318213f56c

Mahler, J. (n.d.). https://www.quora.com/profile/Jess-Burde-Mahler

Mayo Clinic. (2019, September 17). Selective serotonin reuptake inhibitors (ssris). Mayo Clinic; Mayo Clinic. https://www.mayoclinic.org/diseases-conditions/depression/in-depth/ssris/art-20044825

Merriam-Webster. (n.d.). Savant definition & meaning. https://www.merriam-webster.com/dictionary/savant

The most interesting facts about the human nervous system. (n.d.). BYJUS. https://byjus.com/biology/facts-about-nervous-system/

OSMD. (2016, June 10). 4 ways that music and mathematics are related. OSMD. https://www.

omahaschoolofmusicanddance.com/our-blog/4-ways-that-music-and-mathematics-are-related/

Psychology professor jobs. (n.d.). Recruit.net. https://www.recruit.net/job/professor-psychology-jobs/4A0674D7151458CC

Rabbit, M. (2022, December 17). Marc brackett, founder and director of the yale center for emotional intelligence, says doing these 3 things can help you feel safe and seen during the holidays. The Sunday Paper PLUS. https://www.mariashriversundaypaper.com/marc-brackett-founder-and-director-of-the-yale-center-for-emotional-intelligence-says-doing-these-3-things-can-help-you-feel-safe-and-seen-during-the-holidays/

Rudy, L. (2021, June 14). 7 visual tools that can help people with autism learn and thrive. Verywell Health. https://www.verywellhealth.com/visual-thinking-and-autism-5119992#:~:text=Visualspercent20makepercent20itpercent20easierpercent20for

Slate, K. (2022, December 11). 6 signs of insecurity in A relationship you should never ignore. Bonobology. https://bonobologyzz.pages.dev/posts/6-signs-of-insecurity-in-a-relationship-you-should-never-ignore/

Socialthinking - Social thinking. (n.d.). Socialthinking.com. https://www.socialthinking.com/

couriermail.com.au/news/queensland/rockhampton/emma-ward-is-painting-change-for-children-with-autism/news-story/5661ac9924fc9171926f38c77133e52b

Swank, E. (2020, February 7). What are Restricted & Repetitive Behaviors in autism. Autism Assistant. https://autismassistant.com/blog/125/what-are-autism-repetitive-behaviors

Stigma. (n.d.). The Britannica Dictionary. https://www.britannica.com/dictionary/stigma

7 Tips to Help Children With ASD Improve Eye Contact. (2021, December 1). Behavioral-innovations. https://behavioral-innovations.com/blog/children-with-asd-improve-eye-contact/

The stigma of autism: When everyone is staring at you. (2022, April 05). Spark for autism. https://wp.sparkforautism.org/stigma-autism/

Taylor, DJ. (2003). Orwell: A (Brief) Life. Orwell Foundation. https://www.orwellfoundation.com/the-orwell-foundation/orwell/biography/

Team, G. (2011, November 11). Hans Eysenck (1916-1997). Good Therapy. https://www.goodtherapy.org/famous-psychologists/hans-eysenck.html

Thorson, S. (2021, August 19). About Ayres Sensory Integration. Health Children. https://www.healthychildren.org/English/health-issues/conditions/developmental-disabilities/Pages/Sensory-Integration-Therapy.aspx

Uihak, SCC. (2020, July 1). Visual Perception in Autism Spectrum Disorder: A Review of Neuroimaging Studies. NCBI. https://www.ncbi.nlm.nih.gov/pmc/articles/PMC7350544/

Understanding the Different Types of Stimming. (2022, July 15). Experia. https://www.experia-usa.com/blog/understanding-different-types-stimming/

Visual Pathways. (n.d.). Richardsonthebrain. https://www.richardsonthebrain.com/visual-pathways

Villines, Z. (2021, November 28). Everything to Know About Non-Verbal autism. Medical news Today. https://www.medicalnewstoday.com/articles/non-verbal-autism

What is Cognitive Behavioral Therapy? (2022, December 28). Arkview, Recovery. https://www.arkviewrecovery.com/rehab-blog/what-is-cognitive-behavioral-therapy-2/

Welcome to Holland - Interview with Author Emily Perl Holland. (2019, November 4). Cedarstory. https://www.cedarsstory.com/welcome-holland-interview-author-emily-perl-kingsley/

What is sensory integration? (n.d.) Sensory Intergration Education. https://www.sensoryintegrationeducation.com/pages/what-is-si

Wagner, D. (2016, June 27). Polyvagal Theory in Practice. Counceling. https://ct.counseling.org/2016/06/polyvagal-theory-practice/

Weathington, L. (2020, February 18). Neurotypical vs Neurodivergent: What's the Difference? Daivergent. https://daivergent.com/blog/neurotypical-vs-neurodivergent

Wheeler, M. (2020, October 1). Guidelines for Parents on Addressing the Needs of Siblings. Autism Spectrum News. https://autismspectrumnews.org/guidelines-for-parents-on-addressing-the-needs-of-siblings/

Wheeler, M. (n.d.). Siblings perspectives: Some guidelines for parents. IIDC. Retrieved https://www.iidc.indiana.edu/irca/articles/siblings-perspectives-some-guidelines-for-parents.html

Worsley, R. (2022, September 16). Does Learning You are Autistic at an Early Age Lead to Better Adult Outcomes? A Summary for Non-academics. Reframing Autism. https://reframingautism.org.au/does-learning-you-are-autistic-at-a-younger-age-lead-to-better-adult-outcomes-a-summary-for-non-academics/

Why do Autistic People Have Issues with Social Skills? (n.d.) Applied Behavior Analysis https://www.appliedbehavioranalysisedu.org/why-do-autistics-have-issues-with-social-skills/

What is Self-harm? (n.d.). Young Minds. https://www.youngminds.org.uk/young-person/my-feelings/self-harm/

Dear reader

Congratulations on finishing "Autism Communication Keys!"
I hope you found it informative, helpful, and reassuring. I
understand having a child with communication challenges can
sometimes be a source of anxiety and frustration for parents.
My goal with this book was to provide practical tips, insights,
and encouragement to help you navigate this challenging
journey.

If you enjoyed reading "Autism Communication Keys" I would
be immensely grateful if you could take a few minutes to leave
a review on a book review platform such as Goodreads or
Amazon. By sharing your thoughts and feedback, you can help
other parents who may be going through a similar experience
of feeling alone, to feeling more empowered.

Your review could be as simple as a star rating and a sentence
about what you liked about the book or how it helped you.
Whatever you decide to share, know that your review can make
a big difference in helping me reach more families who need
support.

I invite you to visit my website, where you can find more
information about my other books, helpful links, and ways to
contact me. I am always eager to hear from my readers and to
continue the conversation about how I can support children's
communication development.

www.kimgalloslp.com

Printed in Great Britain
by Amazon